Frontispiece.   The Fourth of July valley. Clouds hide the summit of Mount Neva (3906 m). The North Fork of Middle Boulder Creek flows in the foreground. August 9, 1979.

THE FOURTH OF JULY VALLEY

Glacial Geology and Archeology of the Timberline Ecotone

by

James B. Benedict

Research Report No. 2
Center for Mountain Archeology
Ward, Colorado

Preface

One of the most important and elusive goals of climatology is the prediction of future climatic change. Our agriculture, the industrial complex that it supports, and the ever-increasing human population that it is called upon to feed _ all have developed to their present size and character during a century of generous and relatively stable climate. Advance warning of a change to less favorable conditions, such as drought or global cooling, would help us to prepare for the economic and social dislocations that are certain to occur.

At present, there are two principal approaches to climatic forecasting. One approach bases predictions upon the *mechanisms* believed to be responsible for climatic fluctuation, such as changes in the earth's orbital geometry (Hays *et al.* 1976). The other searches the paleoenvironmental record for patterns and periodicities, and extrapolates the trends of the past into the future (Denton and Karlén 1973). This book is a contribution to the second, historical, approach.

The changes in climate that are most likely to affect us as individuals and cultures are those with recurrence intervals of decades, centuries, or a few millenia. If patterns and cycles exist in such high-frequency events, they will not necessarily be recognizable in the palynological record, or in deep-sea cores, or in sea-level chronologies, which tend to be relatively insensitive to short-term climatic fluctuations. However, it may be possible to detect them in the advance-retreat records of small glaciers that are in delicate balance with present-day conditions.

Cirque glaciers in the Indian Peaks of the Colorado Front Range are far south of the principal centers of glacier distribution in North America. They exist in a *non-glacial* regional environment because of highly-favorable topographic and microclimatic conditions (Outcalt 1964, J. Johnson 1979). Due to their small sizes, they respond quickly and sensitively to short-term changes in climate. The record of their past behavior is preserved in a detailed sequence of moraines, which offers excellent opportunities for developing a chronology of glacier advance and retreat.

Two previous chronologies are shown in figure 1; considerable new information has ac-cumulated since their publication. Radiocarbon dates obtained by Madole (1976a, 1980a, 1980b) and Nelson *et al.* (1979) have shown that Pinedale (Wisconsin) valley glaciers began to recede from their terminal moraines as long ago as 14,600 to 13,000 radiocarbon years, and that deglaciation of the mountain crest was complete within a few millenia. Archeological evidence that the eastern foothills of the Rocky Mountains experienced heavy late-winter and spring snowfall on several occasions between 7500 and 5000 yr BP (Benedict 1979a) has opened the possibility of mid-Altithermal glaciation. Studies of soil-profile development and rock weathering (Birkeland and Shroba 1974), and of a radiocarbon-dated lake-sediment core (Davis and Waterman 1979), have raised fundamental questions concerning the reality and dating of the Triple Lakes glacial advances.

The present report is an attempt to refine the glacial chronologies shown in figure 1, and to resolve existing differences of opinion. It is based on a study of moraines, rock glaciers, outwash terraces, and bog deposits in a small (0.5 km^2) sector of the Fourth of July valley, west of Boulder. The study area contains deposits of latest Pinedale to Triple Lakes age, and lichenometric and radiocarbon evidence of snow-bank expansion during Audubon time. Adding interest to the sequence is the fact that two of the moraines were occupied by man during the Altithermal.

Chapter 1 is an introduction to the Fourth of July valley, describing its physical and ecological characteristics and the reasons for its attractiveness to prehistoric man. Chapter 2 is a discussion of the glacial deposits and rock glaciers, stressing radiocarbon dating, lichenometry, and relative-age criteria. Chapters 3 and 4 summarize excavations at the archeological sites, emphasizing the contributions that archeological stratigraphy can make to our understanding of geologic and climatic history. Chapter 5 reviews what has been learned about past Front Range climates, and what remains unknown.

Several peripheral problems are discussed. One is the validity of age assignments based on relative-dating criteria such as soil-profile development, rock weathering, and landform modification. A second is the use of *Rhizocarpon geographicum* s.l., a crustose lichen, for dat-

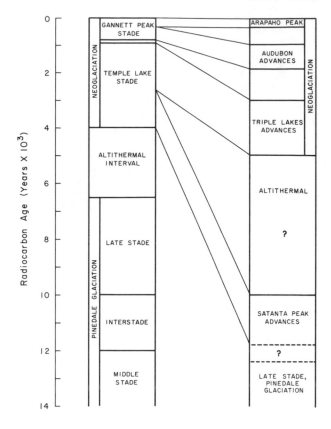

Figure 1. Stages in the development of a Front Range glacial chronology, showing probable corelations.

ing glacial deposits and periods of expanded snowcover. A third is the fate of late Paleo-Indian cultural complexes that disappeared from the High Plains about 7500 radiocarbon years ago, and their possible re-emergence as the McKean complex about 2500 radiocarbon years later. A fourth is the role of the Southern Rocky Mountains as a refuge area for man during dry episodes of the Altithermal.

I excavated the Fourth of July Valley site in 1971, and the Ptarmigan site in 1973, 1974, and 1975. John Eichenour, Byron L. Olson, Karyl Ting, Audrey D. Benedict, Robert J. Benedict, and William L. Benedict participated in site surveys, excavations, and preliminary geologic studies; Elizabeth A. Morris, Katharine T. Benedict, C. Dan Miller, and Jim Gardner provided volunteer help during visits to the sites. Ken Marr assisted during the summer of 1979, which was devoted to glacial geology, bog stratigraphy, and ecological studies. Peter W. Birkeland, Waldemar Chmielewski, Vance T. Holliday, Elizabeth A. Morris, Kenneth L. Pierce, and William E. Scott shared their experience and ideas during a 1979 field conference that led to the development of several new hypotheses; Birkeland, Holliday, Miller, and Morris reviewed chapters of the manuscript, as did John T. Andrews, Audrey D. Benedict, Katharine T. Benedict, and Frank W. Eddy. My thanks to all of the above.

Thanks also to the Boulder District Ranger's office, Roosevelt National Forest, for help in obtaining Antiquities Act permits; to Thomas A. Schmidt, whose reconnaissance study of the valley (Schmidt 1969) first suggested the potential of its glacial record; to James D. Buckley (Teledyne Isotopes) for the consistent high quality of his radiocarbon-age determinations; to Richard G. Baker for macrofossil identification; to Dolores J. Gable for thin-section identification of Tertiary dike rocks used in weathering-rind studies; and to John Chronic and Joe Ben Wheat for advice on lithic sources. Cultural material from excavations in the valley is housed at the University of Colorado Museum (Boulder); artifacts collected at the Fourth of July Valley site in the early 1960s by W.M. Husted were loaned for study through the courtesy of Joe Ben Wheat.

James B. Benedict
Department of Anthropology
Colorado State University
February 23, 1981

Contents

PREFACE v

ABSTRACT 1

CHAPTER 1. THE FOURTH OF JULY VALLEY 3

    Location 3

    Geology 3

    Climate 7

    Vegetation 7

    Archeology 7

CHAPTER 2. QUATERNARY GEOLOGY 10

    Introduction 10

    Dating Methods 11

        Relative Dating 11

        Lichenometry 23

        Archeological Dating 29

        Radiocarbon Dating 29

    The Deposits 31

        Late Pinedale Ground Moraine 31

        Early Satanta Peak Terminal Moraine 33

        Satanta Peak Outwash and Strath Terraces 35

        Late Satanta Peak Terminal Moraine 40

        Ptarmigan Terminal Moraine 41

        Ptarmigan Ablation Moraine 45

        Ptarmigan or Early Triple Lakes Rock Glacier 45

        Late Triple Lakes Rock Glaciers 45

        Sand Ridge 49

        The Fourth of July Valley Bog 53

CHAPTER 3. EXCAVATIONS AT THE FOURTH OF JULY VALLEY SITE 62

    Introduction 62

    Environment 62

    Field Procedures 62

    Stratigraphy and Geologic History 66

    Artifacts 80

    Rock Types 85

    Functional Interpretation of the Projectile Points 85

    The Paleo Indian - McKean Transition 87

Summary 91

CHAPTER 4. EXCAVATIONS AT THE PTARMIGAN SITE 93

Introduction 93

Environment 93

Field Procedures 97

Stratigraphy, Cultural Features, and Geologic History 97

Artifacts 103

Activity Areas 110

Cultural Relationships 113

Summary 114

CHAPTER 5. PALEOCLIMATIC SUMMARY 115

Late Stade, Pinedale Glaciation 115

Satanta Peak Advances 115

Ptarmigan Advance 116

Undated Rock-Glacier Advance 116

Altithermal Soil Formation 117

Early Triple Lakes Advances 117

Late Triple Lakes Advance 117

Audubon Advances 117

Arapaho Peak Advances 118

Conclusions 118

APPENDIX A.   PRINCIPAL ROCK TYPES, SITE 5 BL 120 121

APPENDIX B.   TYPE DESCRIPTIONS OF PROJECTILE POINTS 122

APPENDIX C.   PRINCIPAL ROCK TYPES, SITE 5 BL 170 124

REFERENCES 127

Abstract

THE FOURTH OF JULY VALLEY

The subjects of this book are early man and climatic change; the time framework is the past 12,000 years; the area of study is the ecotone between forest and alpine tundra in the Fourth of July valley, Indian Peaks Wilderness Area, Colorado Front Range.

The valley is eroded in Precambrian igneous and metamorphic bedrock; glacial and periglacial processes have molded its topography. The ecotone region is cold and windy, with moderate to heavy winter snowfall and an abbreviated growing season; snow and soil moisture govern the composition and patterning of plant communities. Prehistoric hunters and gatherers were attracted to the valley by (1) the extent of its timberline ecotone, which provided fuel and shelter and a diversity of plant and animal food resources; (2) dependable stream flow during times of regional drought; (3) access to an important pass across the continental divide; and (4) proximity to tundra grazing areas that were topographically favorable for game-drive hunting. Limiting factors were (1) the absence of local sources of stone that could be used for tool manufacture; and (2) a winter climate so severe that it precluded year-round habitation.

QUATERNARY GEOLOGY

Moraines, rock glaciers, and outwash terraces in the timberline ecotone were mapped and dated; a variety of dating techniques were employed. Weathering-rind thicknesses in fine-textured Tertiary quartz diorite cobbles provided useful age information; other relative-dating criteria, however, lacked the resolution needed for construction of a detailed chronology, were unsuitable for use on deposits as old as those in the study area, or were too strongly affected by environmental factors to give reliable results. A growth-rate curve for the crustose lichen *Rhizocarpon geographicum* s.l. was used to estimate the ages of deposits younger than 3500 years; the long-term growth rate of the species was determined by measuring maximum-diameter lichen thalli on seven radiometrically-dated control surfaces. Time-diagnostic projectile points collected from moraines and outwash terraces provided additional evidence of deposit age. Thirty-three radiocarbon dates were obtained from the 0.5 km² study area; most of the dates cited in this abstract are the weighted means of multiple analyses.

Glacial and bog-stratigraphic studies indicate that (1) outwash associated with the younger of two Satanta Peak terminal moraines in the study area was trenched by the North Fork of Middle Boulder Creek prior to 9215 ± 105 BP, and was blanketed with loess no later than 8270 ± 140 BP; (2) the terminal moraine of a previously unrecognized mid-Altithermal glaciation, the Ptarmigan advance, is older than 6380 ± 95 BP; weathering-rind data suggest deposition between 7250 and 6600 BP; (3) the older of two generations of lobate rock glaciers in the study area is not yet reliably dated; its position in the sequence of deposits suggests that it advanced to its present position during late Ptarmigan or early Triple Lakes time; (4) late Altithermal soil formation is recorded in the study area by redeposited soil humus with a radiocarbon age of 5910 ± 115 years and by an *in situ* A1b horizon that was exposed at the ground surface, and visited by man, ca. 5800-5350 radiocarbon years ago; (5) Altithermal soil formation was followed by two episodes of loess deposition, one older and one younger than 3385 ± 95 BP; (6) a late Triple Lakes lobate rock glacier at the base of the north-facing valley wall advanced rapidly to within a few meters of its modern position between 3340 ± 65 and 2970 ± 65 BP; (7) a ridge of intricately folded and brecciated fine-textured sediments concentric with the front of the rock glacier is a push moraine or loading feature that developed as the lobe of ice and blocky rubble advanced across soft, saturated lake silts and outwash sands; (8) clastic sediments were eroded from the front of the late Triple Lakes rock glacier between 2455 ± 60 and 1845 ± 55 BP, between 1845 ± 55 and 1585 ± 55 BP, and again between *ca.* 1200 and 900 BP; erosion was caused by rock-glacier reactivation and/or destruction of protective vegetation during episodes of Audubon snowbank expansion; (9) preliminary results of an experimental study of lichen mortality indicate that near-total destruction of lichen communities on the floor of the valley during Audubon time could have been caused by a relatively *minor* increase in the duration of general snow cover.

THE FOURTH OF JULY VALLEY SITE

The Fourth of July Valley site (5 BL 120) is an Early Archaic campsite on the outer of three terminal moraines in the study area. Its altitude is 3415 m. Deposits in the 41 m^2 excavation area include early Satanta Peak till, proglacial lake sediments, and late Satanta Peak outwash. Satanta Peak deposits were deformed by ice-core melting, eroded by the North Fork of Middle Boulder Creek, and buried by colluvium, slopewash sediments, and loess. The site was occupied 5960 ± 85 radiocarbon years ago, prior to arrival of the late Triple Lakes rock glacier that now stands at its southern margin. Artifacts were extensively redeposited by mass-wasting processes during Audubon time. The character of the tool and waste-flake assemblage suggests that a small party of hunters camped briefly on the moraine to replace broken projectile points and to process game. Projectile points are believed to be intermediate in the development of McKean Lanceolate and Duncan points from late Paleo-Indian forms such as James Allen and Pryor Stemmed points; they include stemmed and lanceolate specimens, some of which show parallel-oblique flaking, alternate edge retouch, and burination. The site is one of a growing number of excavated high-altitude occupation sites that document an influx of people into the Front Range from low-altitude environments during a severe late Altithermal drought.

THE PTARMIGAN SITE

The Ptarmigan site (5 BL 170) is a multiple-component campsite at 3460-m elevation. Excavation of a 43 m^2 area exposed ground moraine of Ptarmigan age, alluvium, colluvium, slopewash sediments, and loess. Artifacts could not be separated stratigraphically because of vertical frost sorting. However, several artifact styles could be related to radiocarbon-dated tool-resharpening areas by means of shared distinctive rock types. Corner-notched projectile points believed to have evolved from the Mount Albion Corner-notched style are assigned to a Middle Archaic component dated at 4690 ± 55 BP. A side-notched projectile point with similarities to

the Bitterroot and Logan Creek styles is tentatively assigned to an Early Archaic component dated at 6380 ± 95 BP; the latter brings to *four* the number of cultural complexes that are known to have been present above timberline in the Indian Peaks during the Altithermal.

PALEOCLIMATIC SUMMARY

Data from geological and archeological studies in the Fourth of July valley and adjoining areas suggest that glaciers and/or rock glaciers have advanced a minimum of eleven times since disappearance of Pinedale valley glaciers from the region. The concept of "Neoglaciation", as envisioned by Porter and Denton (1967), is not applicable to the Front Range, nor is the sequence of "modified Blytt-Sernander" climatic episodes (Bryson *et al.* 1970) used as a paleoenvironmental standard by many Plains archeologists. Patterns and cycles such as those hypothesized by Denton and Karlén (1973) cannot be recognized in the glacial record, suggesting that the causes of post-Pinedale glaciation in the Front Range were aperiodic, and precluding use of the chronology for predicting future climatic change.

1

The Fourth of July Valley

Location

The Fourth of July valley is in Boulder County, north-central Colorado. It is the northernmost drainage in the headwaters of Middle Boulder Creek, a tributary to the South Platte River system. The valley is part of the Indian Peaks Wilderness Area, a congeries of 4000-m-high summits, ragged arêtes, windswept tundra uplands, clearwater streams and lakes, cirque glaciers and forests directly south of Rocky Mountain National Park. It is bounded to the north and west by the continental divide (Fig. 2). Mount Neva (3906 m) is the principal summit on the western skyline, and South Arapaho Peak (4083 m) the principal summit visible to the northeast. Between these mountains is Arapaho Pass (3629 m), a tundra saddle that in prehistoric times was the most heavily-utilized east-west travel route in an 18-km sector of continental divide. From Arapaho Pass, old trails lead northward and westward to the sagebrush grasslands of Middle Park, and southeastward to the mesas, hogbacks, and shortgrass plains near Boulder (Ives 1942).

The study area (Figs. 2, 3) is reached most easily from the Fourth of July Campground, 8-9 km northwest of the town of Eldora. The route is shown on U.S.G.S. Nederland, East Portal, and Monarch Lake 7.5-minute quadrangle maps. From the campground parking area an improved trail leads 2.9 km to the Fourth of July Mine (Figs. 2, 3), where tailings, a rusty boiler, and remnants of an old shafthouse remain from early mining days[1]. Here the trail is abandoned in favor of a cross-country route southwestward through interconnected meadows to the valley floor. The total distance from trailhead to study area is a little over 4 km.

[1] A shallow cirque and col north of the mine, referred to as the "Fourth of July Cirque" in several publications (Mahaney 1973a, 1973b, Williams 1973, Anderson 1978), lies outside the area discussed in this report.

Geology

The Fourth of July valley is eroded in Precambrian biotite gneiss, granodiorite, quartz monzonite, and granite (Pearson and Johnson 1980, Pl. I). Outcrops of amphibolite, pegmatite, and quartz diorite are also present, but are too small to be shown on existing geologic maps. The study area is 5-6 km west of the Caribou stock, one of nine large Tertiary intrusives that define the western margin of the Front Range Mineral Belt (Lovering and Goddard 1950).

The principal structural element in the valley is a northwest-trending fault that extends from the Caribou mining district across the continental divide to the head of Meadow Creek (Pearson and Johnson 1980). The fault is the most plausible explanation for the existence of Arapaho Pass, and for a 150-m difference in the mean altitude of the mountain crest north and south of its course. The highest summits in the Indian Peaks are on the north side of the fault. According to Pearson and Johnson (1980), displacement may have occurred along the fault as recently as the late Tertiary.

During Bull Lake and early to middle Pinedale time, glaciers originating in Fourth of July valley snowfields coalesced with glaciers from other tributary valleys in the Middle Boulder Creek drainage, advancing southeastward to the present town of Nederland, where they deposited terminal and recessional moraines at altitudes of 2500-2580 m (Millett 1956, Bonnett 1970). Moraines of the late stage of Pinedale Glaciation are higher in the valley, at an altitude of approximately 3000-3050 m.

Except for perched erratic boulders and patchy accumulations of ground moraine, Bull Lake and Pinedale glacial advances left no depositional record above present timberline. Erosion, rather than deposition, characterized the study area during this interval. Subglacial scouring accentuated the grain of the gneissic bedrock, smoothing and striating the up-valley sides of knobs and ridges, and

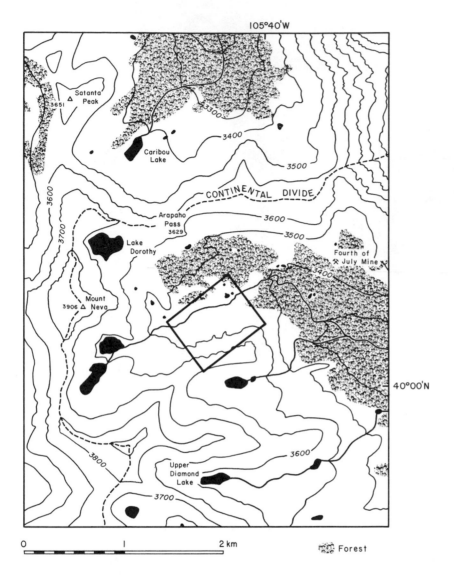

105°40'W

40°00'N

0   1   2 km

Forest

Figure 2. Map of the Arapaho Pass area. Topography and forest distribution are from USGS Monarch Lake and East Portal quadrangle maps; krummholz spruce and fir trees grow at higher elevations. Contour interval 100 m. The location of the Fourth of July valley study area is shown by the small rectangle.

plucking joint-block boulders from their down-valley sides. Separating the knobs and ridges are intersecting linear swales that mark old fault and fracture lines and weakly-resistant metamorphic units (Fig. 3). The swales contain bogs and small ponds, late-lying snowbanks, and grassy meadows. Each is a private place, with a character of its own.

Throughout most of its course the valley is deeply U-shaped in cross section, locally with high valley-side benches. Erratic boulders, lateral-moraine remnants, and truncated spurs record maximum ice depths on the order of 250-325 m. The longitudinal profile of the Fourth of July valley, like other glaciated valleys in the Front Range (Colman 1976), is a series of broad steps, separated by steeply-sloping risers. Each step is narrower and more-nearly horizontal than the step directly below it. Moraine-dammed cirque lakes occur on the uppermost step, which is entirely above tree limit. The study area and major prehistoric campsites in the valley are on the second-highest step, in the forest-tundra eco-

tone. Bedrock steps at lower altitudes are densely forested, and have produced relatively little evidence of prehistoric occupation.

Moraines and rock glaciers in cirques north and south of the summit of Mount Neva (Fig. 4) have not yet been studied in detail; cursory observations suggest that the oldest are of Satanta Peak age (Fig. 1), and that at least three younger episodes of cirque-glacier advance are represented. Deposits at the base of the south wall of the valley (Fig. 5) have been studied intensively (Chapter 2); they indicate that glaciers and snowfields developed independently of the Neva cirques on a number of occasions during post-Pinedale time.

Small-scale periglacial landforms add to the geomorphic complexity of the study area. The floors of several late-lying snowbanks are paved with close-packed boulders (White 1972), heaved to the surface by frost and pressed to a common level by the weight of snow. Active sorted nets (Washburn 1980) occur where boulder pavements are intruded from below by plugs of fine-textured earth, and on

Figure 3. Vertical aerial photograph of the Fourth of July valley study area, September 1, 1970. The trail to Arapaho Pass is a wagon road, constructed between 1904 and 1910 in an attempt to connect Boulder and Grand Counties (Black 1969). The wagon road was never completed.

Figure 4. View of Mount Neva from Arapaho Pass. Exposed in the cirque headwall are Precambrian biotite gneiss (PЄbg), Boulder Creek granite (PЄbc), and Silver Plume granite (PЄsp); the latter is an "indicator" rock type on deposits in the study area. Three ages of moraines and rock glaciers (numbered 1 to 3, from youngest to oldest) occur in the cirque; a fourth moraine (4) forms the north shore of Lake Dorothy. The line of boulders in the foreground is a game-drive wall, part of archeological site 5 BL 114. October 4, 1978.

Figure 5. View of the Fourth of July valley study area from the trail to Arapaho Pass. Lobate rock glaciers of late Triple Lakes age tower above Ptarmigan and Satanta Peak terminal moraines on the valley floor. The area in the foreground was last glaciated during late Pinedale time; it illustrates the topographic and vegetational diversity of the timberline ecotone region. September 22, 1972.

the floors of shallow ponds. Solifluction lobes (Benedict 1970) are present on slopes that are saturated in fall.

Climate

The study area is cool, moist, and windy, with moderate to heavy winter accumulation of wind-drifted snow. Mean July, January, and annual air temperatures, extrapolated from U.S. Weather Bureau sources and from data in Ives (1953), Marr *et al.* (1968), Marr and Marr (1973), and Barry (1973), are 10°C, -11 °C, and -1°C, respectively. Wind velocities are high, but because of the protection provided by trees and topography are unlikely to equal the average annual velocity of 10.3 m/sec (23 mph) recorded above tree limit on Niwot Ridge, 6 km to the northeast (Barry 1973). Strong winds are always from the west or northwest, but precipitation can come from almost any direction, and the sky above the study area is the scene of frequent confrontation between opposing storm systems. Average annual precipitation at this altitude is 850-900 mm (Benedict and Olson 1978, Fig. 6); *effective* precipitation in the study area can be expected to be higher, due to a significant influx of windblown snow from surrounding uplands. Winter snow builds dunes and corniced drifts that cover all but the tops of trees, rock glaciers, and the highest bedrock knobs (Fig. 6). Many snowbanks persist throughout the summer and fall, supplying meltwater to the trickles, seeps, and tiny ponds that are important elements in the ecological diversity of the valley.

Vegetation

The second-highest bedrock step (Figs. 3, 5) is broad and gently sloping, and corresponds closely in altitude (3365-3535 m) to the altitude of the timberline ecotone[2]. This coincidence has resulted in an unusually extensive zone of mixture between forest and tundra species. Tree islands of Engelmann spruce (*Picea engelmannii*) and subalpine fir (*Abies lasiocarpa*) grow in well-drained sites where winter snow is deep enough to protect their needles from desiccation, but not so deep or long-lasting that seedlings are destroyed by snow molds, mechanical stresses, or inability to complete growth and hardening (Wardle 1974). Limber pines (*Pinus flexilis*) cling to the rocky soil of windier locales; seedlings of lodgepole pine (*Pinus contorta*)

grow in small numbers on the valley floor, far above the normal altitudinal range of this species.

The distribution of plant communities in the Fourth of July valley study area is governed primarily by the length of the snow-free growing season and the availability of moisture, the effects of which cannot always be separated. Factors such as soil instability and small-mammal disturbance are important in specialized localities. The influence of rock type is minor, and the influence of slope orientation is important only to the extent that it governs winter snowdrift patterns.

In well-drained, windy sites with little or no accumulation of winter snow, the mountain dryad (*Dryas octopetala*) and two turf-forming sedges (*Kobresia myosuroides* and *Carex rupestris*) are important; such environments comprise only a small portion of the study area. In wetter, more-protected habitats there are lush streamside herb communities, seasonally-submerged moss mats, *Sphagnum* hummocks, willow thickets, and sedge meadows. Areas that remained covered with snow until late August or September, and that are irrigated by meltwater during the short snow-free growing season, are bare and frost-disturbed. Drier snow-accumulation areas support communities in which sedges (*Carex pyrenaica*, *C. nigricans*), the black-headed daisy (*Erigeron melanocephalus*), Drummond's rush (*Juncus drummondii*), sibbaldia (*Sibbaldia procumbens*), and tufted hairgrass (*Deschampsia caespitosa*) are important.

Archeology

The Fourth of July valley has become a special favorite of all of us who have worked there. Contributing to its appeal are the diversity of its microenvironments and the unusual extent (1½-2 km[2]) of its resource-rich timberline ecotone. Less easily put into words are the intangibles: the "earth and the great weather" in their endless variety; the glare of snow and ever-present sound of running water; the rockpile warning cries of pikas and

[2] *"Timberline" refers to the upper limit of forest growth, and "tree limit" to the upper limit of tree survival. The "timberline ecotone" is the zone of transition between forest and tundra plant communities, and is characterized by islands of stunted spruce and fir trees (Marr 1977) in a matrix of alpine tundra vegetation. Plant names used in this report follow the fifth edition of W.A. Weber's* Rocky Mountain Flora *(Weber 1976). Ecological studies of the Front Range alpine region include those of Marr (1961), Komárková (1979), and Willard (1979).*

Figure 6. Mount Neva from the study area, April 27, 1970. The field of view is approximately the same as in the frontispiece.

marmots; the patent-leather joy of ravens in the Neva cirques.

Our archeological surveys indicate that others, before us, have shared the opinion that this is a valley with particularly good medicine. We have recorded 25 prehistoric sites (5.4 sites per km^2) above timberline in the valley, mostly within the forest-tundra ecotone. Several of the sites are extensive, and have been occupied repeatedly. A similarly high density of sites (5.2 per km^2) has been recorded above timberline in the Caribou Lake valley, north of Arapaho Pass (Fig. 2). Remnants of a prehistoric trail, still locally visible, suggest that travel across the continental divide was an important reason for human utilization of both areas; however, stone game-drive structures on the upland surface south of Arapaho Pass (Fig. 4) and on the tundra slopes above and below Lake Dorothy show that early people were also attracted to the area by the opportunities that it offered for communal hunting of large game animals.

Artifacts from sites above timberline in the Fourth of July and Caribou Lake valleys document a long history of human use, beginning with occupation of the Caribou Lake site (5 GA 22) by people of the Cody complex about 8460 ± 140 radiocarbon years ago (I-5449, Benedict 1974), and continuing into Late Prehistoric time. According to local legend the Lake Dorothy area, astride the pass, was a neutral zone in which Arapahos and Uncompah-

gre Utes met peacefully for trade (Ives 1942).

All but a few of the food resources and raw materials needed by early hunters and gatherers in order to live comfortably in the mountains in summer and fall are available in the Fourth of July valley study area. Fuel and protection from the wind are provided by spruce and fir tree islands. Blueberries (*Vaccinium myrtillus*, *V. scoparium*) and creeping wintergreen berries (*Gaultheria humifusa*) mature in September, remaining on the low bushes until early October; Colorado currants (*Ribes coloradense*) ripen in sunny openings among the tree islands. Potherbs such as fern-leaved lovage (*Ligusticum filicinum*), fireweed (*Chamerion angustifolium*), marsh marigold (*Caltha leptosepala*), and alpine sorrel (*Oxyria digyna*) are abundant on the valley floor; American bistort (*Bistorta bistortoides*) is a ubiquitous starchy rootcrop, and the fleshy edible roots of the alpine spring beauty (*Claytonia megarhiza*) can be gathered in quantity on nearby summits.

Mule deer (*Odocoileus hemionus*) make heavy use of the valley in summer and fall. Elk (*Cervus canadensis*) have become fully reestablished since their extermination by early settlers; bighorn (*Ovis canadensis*), however, have been unable to significantly repopulate the area. I have observed pine marten (*Martes americana*), short- and long-tailed weasel (*Mustela erminea*, *M. frenata*), coyote (*Canis latrans*), and red fox (*Vulpes vulpes*) in the study area, and black bear (*Ursus americanus*),

mountain lion (*Felis concolor*), and bobcat
(*Lynx rufus*) nearby. Common small mammals and
game birds that are likely to have been hunted by early visitors to the valley include
the yellow-bellied marmot (*Marmota flavivent-
ris*), porcupine (*Erethizon dorsatum*), white-
tailed ptarmigan (*Lagopus leucurus*), and blue
grouse (*Dendrogapus obscurus*). Chewed twigs
record the presence of beaver (*Castor canadensis*) in streamside willow thickets at the eastern end of the study area during decades
past, although not in recent years.

It is difficult to imagine a shortage of
water ever preventing human use of the Fourth
of July valley. The North Fork of Middle Boulder Creek (*frontispiece*) is a rushing mountain brook, fed by perennial snowfields in
the shelter of the continental divide. Too
small for trout in its reaches above timberline, the North Fork tumbles over rust-brown
boulders spackled with dipper droppings. The
creek and its tributary streams are dependable sources of water even in dry years, although deeply buried by snow in winter and
spring (Fig. 6).

One factor that may have restricted prehistoric use of the valley to relatively
short visits was the absence of local sources
of stone that could be used to replace worn-
out and broken tools. Orthoquartzite that outcrops in "sandstone dikes" along the Arapaho
Pass Fault (Pearson and Johnson 1980) has a
blocky, rather than conchoidal, fracture, and
is unsuitable for chipped-stone tool manufacture. Except for poor-quality vein quartz,
utilized by people of the Mount Albion complex (Benedict and Olson 1978) but ignored by
other prehistoric groups, no usable lithic
materials are available within 25 km of the
study area. The nearest known sources of
chert, petrified wood, and workable quartzite
are in Middle Park and the Denver Basin. The
nearest sources of sandstone for grinding
tools are in the Boulder area.

Because of the severe winter climate of
the valley, it is unlikely that year-round
occupation was practical even at times of regional warmth. Depending upon winter storm
patterns, seasonal animal movements, and the
geographic experience and individual prefer-
ences of the human groups involved, winters
were spent in the foothills to the east or in
sheltered valleys on Colorado's western slope.

2

Quaternary Geology

Introduction

The purposes of geologic field work in the valley were (1) to reconstruct the environments of archeological sites as they existed at times of prehistoric occupation; (2) to strengthen and revise the chronology of Front Range cirque glaciation; and (3) to evaluate the effectiveness of available techniques for differentiating and dating deposits in the difficult late Pinedale-Triple Lakes time range.

A geologic map of the study area (Fig. 7) was completed in 1979. Age assignments were based on position in the valley, weathering-rind thicknesses, lichen diameters, archeological associations, and radiocarbon dating. The oldest Quaternary map unit in the study area (Pgm) is ground moraine exposed by ice retreat at the close of the late stage of Pinedale Glaciation; the youngest (TLrg) is an apron of coalescing lobate rock glaciers and talus deposits of late Triple Lakes and younger age.

Directions of ice movement were determined from the distributions of indicator rock types such as Silver Plume granite (Fig. 4), and from the orientations of glacial striations on bedrock outcrops (Fig. 7). As many as three superimposed sets of glacially-produced scratches and grooves are locally preserved (Fig. 8); changes in their orientations document a shift from easterly to northerly flow during the early part of the postglacial interval, implying the progressive restriction of snowfields to north-facing exposures as a result of rising summer temperatures.

Several of the terms used in this paper require definition. Others that were used previously (Richmond 1965, Benedict 1973*a*), but are no longer appropriate, require explanation.

The term "advance" is used in preference to "stade" because the latter is a subdivision of a glaciation (Flint 1971: 374), whereas the moraines and rock glaciers discussed in this report were deposited during an interglaciation. An advance is simply a period of time in which glaciers and snowbanks were more extensive than they are today. Advances are named for geographic landmarks near the deposits where they were first recognized. The names are local and informal; time boundaries can be adjusted as new data require.

The names "Arapaho Peak", "Audubon", "Triple Lakes", and "Satanta Peak" are retained from an earlier study (Fig. 1). The name "Ptarmigan" is introduced for an advance that was not previously recognized; its type locality is a moraine northeast of the Ptarmigan site (Chapter 4), where weathering-rind data and radiocarbon dates provide an indication of its age.

The term "Neoglaciation" (Fig. 1) is abandoned as a subdivision of the Front Range glacial chronology because it cannot be recognized in the local glacial record. Defined by Porter and Denton (1967: 205) as "the climatic episode characterized by rebirth and/or growth of glaciers following maximum shrinkage during the Hypsithermal interval", the term implies both a climatic event and a glacial response. The climatic event (an interval of late-postglacial cooling) is widely recognized, although its importance in the Colorado Rockies is uncertain (Maher 1973); the glacial response, in the Front Range, was a continuation of business as usual, with glaciers advancing and retreating intermittently as they had done during the preceding 6000 years, but with ever-decreasing amplitude. A practical difficulty with applying Porter and Denton's definition of Neoglaciation to the Front Range sequence is that "maximum shrinkage" (i.e., total or near-total disappearance of glaciers) occurred on at least five separate occasions during post-Pinedale time.

The term "Altithermal" (Antevs 1948) is used in this paper for the warmest part of the postglacial temperature curve, as reconstructed from pollen diagrams and other evidence of long-term climatic change. It is synonymous with "Hypsithermal" (Deevey and Flint 1957), as re-defined by Wright (1976), but is preferred because it was the earlier of the two terms to be-introduced, and does not require major surgery to bring it into line with modern usage[3]. The effects of the Altithermal on man are controversial (Huscher and Huscher 1941, Antevs 1948, Aschmann 1958, Bryan and Gruhn 1964, Jennings 1964, Baumhoff and Heizer 1965, Hurt 1966, Husted 1970, Bense 1971, C. Nance 1972, Reeves 1973, Fagan 1974, Knox 1976, Benedict 1979a). Most archeologists in the Colorado-Wyoming region equate the Altithermal with the Early Plains Archaic Period (Frison 1978), date it at approximately 7500 to 5000 radiocarbon years BP, and agree that it had at least a modicum of influence on early man.

The term "Holocene", like Neoglaciation, is abandoned in this paper. Defined by Hageman (1972) and Mörner (1976) as the period of earth history that began 10,000 radiocarbon years ago, the term has no climatic significance in the Colorado Rockies; it cannot be used as a synonym for the present interglaciation, which began thousands of years earlier, both in the Front Range (Madole 1976a) and elsewhere(Mercer 1972). Rather than use the term in its inelastic formal sense, leaving 3000-4000 years of postglacial time unaccounted for, I will refer here instead to the "postglacial", or "post-Pinedale", interval.

Dating Methods

RELATIVE DATING

Relative-dating techniques have been used in the mountains of the western United States for almost half a century (Blackwelder 1931). They are the *only* basis for the majority of glacial chronologies in the region, and a *principal* basis for many of the remainder. Birkeland *et al.* (1979b: 542) consider them to be "the most useful and objective" means of subdividing, classifying, and correlating alpine glacial deposits.

The underlying assumption of all relative-dating methods is that *time* can be recognized in the clutter of variables that affect post-depositional modification of moraines

---

[3] *Antevs' (1948) concept of the Altithermal is closely similar to Wright's (1976) and to my own (Benedict 1979a). He viewed it as a geologic-climate unit with time-transgressive boundaries, marked by a rise in mean temperature to above modern levels, but with superimposed short-term temperature oscillations. Aridity was not an ingredient of Antevs' original definition because "moisture conditions are too regional to be used as a basis for a general time division" (Antevs 1948: 176).*

and rock glaciers. In the mountains of western North America, where altitudinal and environmental contrasts are strong, a competitive hypothesis might be that the effects of time will be obscured by the effects of climate, microclimate, and vegetation.

If relative-dating techniques will work under *any* circumstances, they should work in the Fourth of July valley study area, which has a limited range of altitudes, rock types, snow-accumulation regimes, and plant communities. Criteria tested in the study area are discussed below. Numerical data are summarized in figure 9.

Moraine Dissection. Differences in the widths and depths of stream channels eroded in moraines have been used by R. Nelson (1954), Breckenridge (1969), Carrara and Andrews (1975), and others as indicators of relative age. In the Fourth of July valley study area, meltwater from perennial snowbanks crosses the late Triple Lakes rock-glacier apron and bouldery Ptarmigan moraine through subsurface drainageways, deep within the deposits (Fig. 7). Emerging in springs at the front of the Ptarmigan moraine, it flows to the floor of the valley in a series of sub-parallel rivulets, shallowly eroded in late Satanta Peak till. The discharges of these streams are minor in comparison to the discharge of the North Fork of Middle Boulder Creek, which crosses the early Satanta Peak terminal moraine through a channel *ca.* 20 m wide, and 3-3.5 m deep.

Differences in moraine dissection in the study area can be explained entirely by differences in the boulderiness of the deposits and the discharges and hydrologic histories of the streams that cross them. Time may also have been a factor; however, its contribution cannot be assessed. Graf (1971) reached a similar conclusion in the Beartooth Mountains.

Vascular Plant Cover. Newly-deposited moraines and freshly-deglaciated land surfaces are free of vegetation; colonization by pioneer plant species begins immediately, and proceeds through "an environmentally conditioned series of invasions" (Matthews 1978: 174) until a climax community has developed. In the Front Range alpine region, noticeable changes in species composition continue to occur for several thousand years. They can be used to separate and correlate deposits of Arapaho Peak, Audubon, and Triple Lakes age (Mahaney 1974), but not older deposits. Primary plant succession has ended on moraines in the study area; vascular plant communities are in dynamic equilibrium with existing environmental conditions except in areas of recent disturbance.

Maximum Lichen Cover. Differences in percent lichen cover have been used as evidence of deposit age by Benedict (1968), Birkeland (1973), C. Miller (1973), Williams (1973), and others. A visual estimate of percent lichen cover was made for the most heavily lichen-covered boulder on each deposit; values are plotted in fig-

| LATE STADE, PINEDALE GLACIATION | Pgm | Ground moraine, late Pinedale age. Bedrock is present at shallow depth. |
| PRECAMBRIAN | PЄbg | Precambrian bedrock, largely biotite gneiss, with scattered erratic boulders and unmappable patches of ground moraine. |

Flow lobe in ablation moraine

Striation direction

Spring

Stream

Lake or pond

Bog and floodplain sediments, undifferentiated

TRIPLE LAKES ADVANCE	TLsr	"Sand ridge", formed as a push moraine or by loading of lake and outwash sediments during rock-glacier advance.
	TLrg	Rock glacier and talus, late Triple Lakes age and younger.
	rg	Rock glacier, intermediate in age between Ptarmigan ground moraine and late Triple Lakes rock glaciers.
PTARMIGAN ADVANCE	PTam	Ablation moraine, formed by rockfall onto Ptarmigan glacier.
	PTgm	Ground moraine, largely of Ptarmigan age. Bedrock is present at shallow depth.
	PTm	End moraine, Ptarmigan age.
SATANTA PEAK ADVANCES	SPo	Outwash terrace, late Satanta Peak age.
	SPt	End and ground moraine, early Satanta Peak age, planed to level of late Satanta Peak outwash by lateral stream erosion.
	SPm2	End moraine, late Satanta Peak age.
	SPm1	End moraine, early Satanta Peak age.

Figure 7. Geologic map of the Fourth of July valley study area. The aerial photograph was taken on September 9, 1970. The map area is shown by the rectangles in figures 2 and 3.

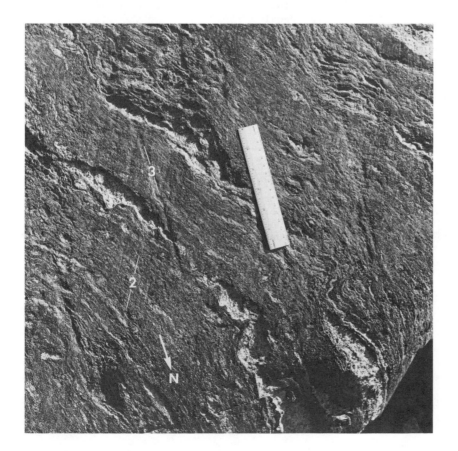

Figure 8. Striated bedrock E of the Ptarmigan site. Three sets of grooves and striations are present: their mean orientations are (1) N 74°E, (2) N 38°E, and (3) N 3°E. Set 1, the oldest, is believed to be of Pinedale age because, like striations in parts of the study area that were last glaciated during Pinedale time (Fig. 7), it is oriented parallel to the axis of the valley. Set 2 is believed to be of Satanta Peak age because striations with similar orientations occur in parts of the study area that were last glaciated by Satanta Peak ice (Fig. 7). Set 3 is thought to be of Ptarmigan age because it represents the youngest episode of glacial abrasion on the outcrop, and because its orientation is consistent with flow to the Ptarmigan terminal moraine. Striations are well preserved at this locality because biotite layers in the gneiss are closely spaced, inhibiting granular disintegration.

ure 9a. Lichen cover does not permit diffe-
rentiation of deposits as old as those in the
study area because lichen communities have already reached full development. Areas of
sparse lichen growth on deposits older than
about 3000 yr are in most cases the result of
late-lying snow, present or past.

Rock-Glacier Front Angles. The minimum and
maximum slope angles of rock-glacier fronts
were measured with a Brunton compass (Fig.
9b). Front angles steeper than the angle of
repose for talus are an indication of ongoing
movement, faster at the surface of the rock
glacier than at depth (Wahrhaftig and Cox
1959). Movement may indicate that a rock glacier is too young to have experienced important ice-core melting; however, it is rarely
possible to rule out the influence of age-
independent factors such as differences in
slope and exposure, initial ice content, and
the thickness and albedo of insulating debris.

Distal Slope Angles of End Moraines. A relationship between the distal slopes of end moraines and their ages has been suggested for
deposits in the Beartooth Mountains (Graf
1971), Medicine Bow Mountains (Kiver 1972),
and Sawatch Range (C. Miller 1979). Distal
slope angles were measured at five or more
localities on each moraine in the Fourth of
July valley study area (Fig. 9b). Steepness
was found to be correlated much more closely
with boulderiness than with deposit age. All
distal slope angles recorded in the study
area, from steepest to gentlest, can be duplicated along the outer slope of the early
Satanta Peak end moraine.

Boulder Frequency. Boulder frequency is defined as the number of exposed boulders larger than 30 cm that lie within 1 m on either
side of a 50-m-long tape stretched taut
along the moraine crest, rock-glacier surface, or outwash surface. Because of a size-
able edge effect, boulder frequency is better
envisioned as a dimensionless index than as
the actual number of boulders in a 100 m^2
area. Boulder frequency is a function of many
variables in addition to the time available
for weathering processes to break large boulders into small. In the study area it ranges
from as little as 9, on an outwash terrace
composed primarily of cobbles and blanketed
by loess, to as much as 643, on an active
rock glacier without surface fines. Considerable variation can occur along the crest
of a single moraine (Fig. 9c), supporting
the conclusion of C. Miller and Birkeland
(1974) and Oviatt (1977) that boulderiness
is an unreliable indicator of age.

Percent Weathered Granitic Boulders. A
"weathered" granitic boulder is a boulder
with the texture and approximate mineralogy
of granite, and a surface on which individual mineral grains stand in relief; a boulder is "weathered" if any portion of its surface shows such alteration[4]. An effort was

made to locate and examine at least 100 granitic boulders on each deposit; smaller samples were necessary on three deposits (Ptarmigan ablation moraine and two late Triple Lakes
rock glaciers) that consisted almost exclusively of gneiss.

In nearby valleys, I have found that the
percentage of boulders that show evidence of
surface weathering increases with relative age
on deposits of Triple Lakes age and younger.
In the study area, however, all deposits can
be characterized as weathered (Fig. 9d); the
few fresh boulders that are present have fall-
en from surrounding cliffs or from the fronts
of rock glaciers, or have been brought to the
surface from depth by frost action, exposed by
marmot burrowing or stream erosion, or insula-
ted from the surface weathering environment by
persistent snow.

Maximum Depth of Differential Weathering.
Depths of differential weathering have been
used for relative-age dating by Mahaney
(1973a), Williams (1973), C. Miller and Birkeland (1974), Carroll (1974), and others. They
can be used in the Indian Peaks to distinguish
between Audubon deposits (slightly pitted) and
Triple Lakes or older deposits (deeply pitted),
a distinction that is particularly useful in
areas of Audubon-age lichen kill. Their value
is otherwise seriously limited by the influence of environmental factors.

Differential weathering is strongly affected by differences in altitude. Below present timberline, weathering pits rarely attain
depths greater than a few centimeters, even on
Pinedale and Bull Lake deposits. Above timberline, however, medium- and coarse-textured
granular rocks weather so rapidly that their
surfaces can become cavernously pitted after
only a few thousand years of exposure (Benedict 1970). Biotite-rich metamorphic layers
and mafic inclusions weather more slowly, and
stand in relief (Fig. 10), indicating that
differential weathering in the alpine environment is primarily a mechanical process.

Birkeland (1973) has attributed poor development of weathering pits in the subalpine
and montane forests to fire, a non-climatic
factor that causes spalling of rock surfaces.
However, altitudinal effects also occur on
bouldery taluses that are unlikely to have
ever been forested or burned. Altitudinal variations in freeze-thaw frequency (Fig. 11) are
a possible explanation, as are differences in
the importance of hydration shattering (White
1976a). Differences in lichen cover related to
altitude are a third possible explanation, although it is not clear whether the effects of
lichens are more likely to be disruptive (Fry
1927) or protective and insulative.

---

[4] *A more satisfactory approach would have been
to estimate the percentage of the surface of
each boulder that was weathered, rather than
making a simple weathered/non-weathered distinction.*

16

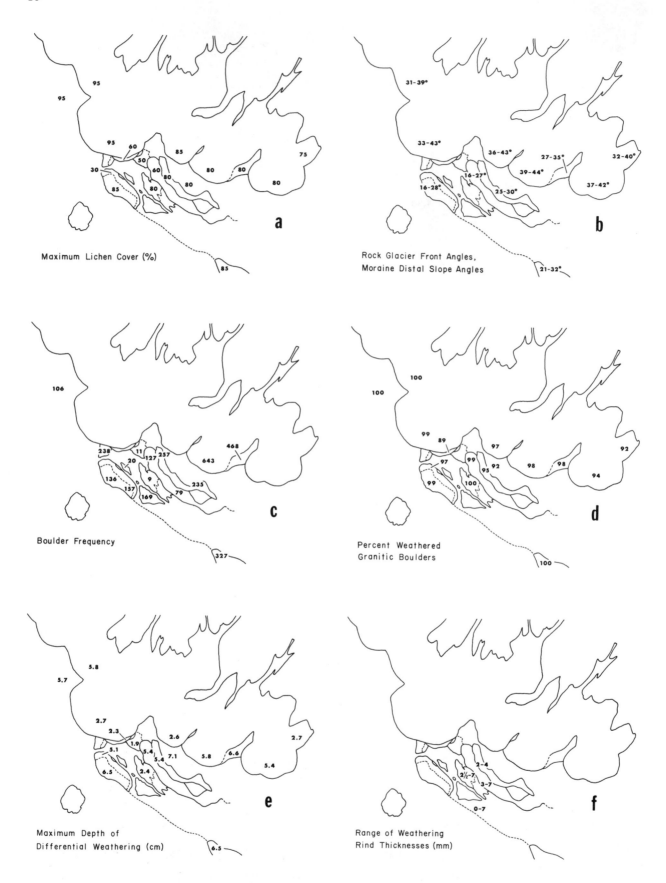

Figure 9. Relative-age data, Fourth of July valley study area.

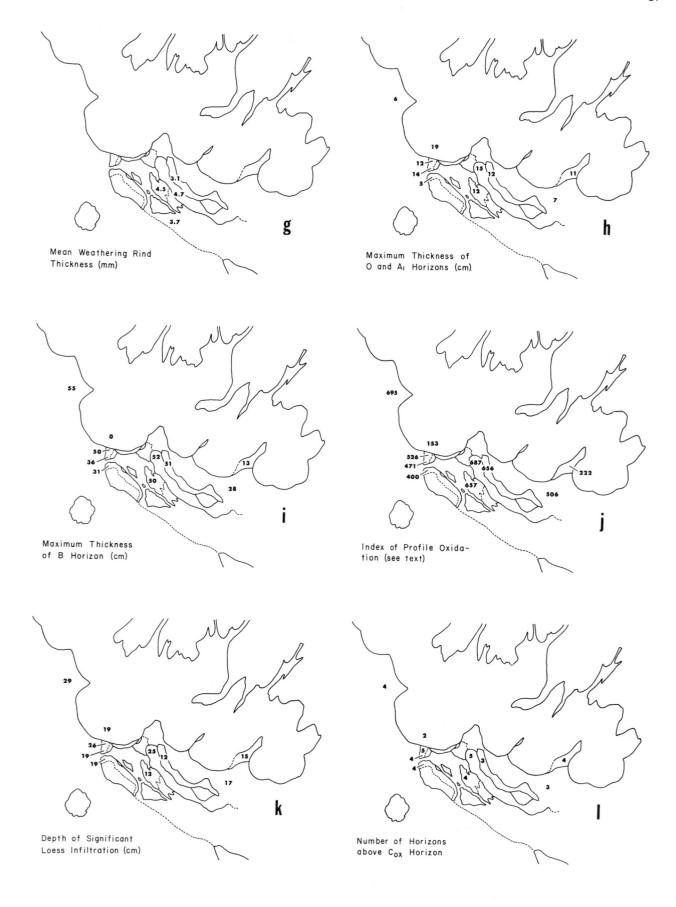

g

Mean Weathering Rind
Thickness (mm)

h

Maximum Thickness of
O and A₁ Horizons (cm)

i

Maximum Thickness
of B Horizon (cm)

j

Index of Profile Oxida-
tion (see text)

k

Depth of Significant
Loess Infiltration (cm)

l

Number of Horizons
above C_{OX} Horizon

Figure 10. Differential weathering of Precambrian biotite gneiss, Ptarmigan ablation moraine (PTam). A 15-cm rule provides scale. Weathering has removed quartz and plagioclase grains to a maximum depth of 5.8 cm, leaving biotite-rich layers relatively unaltered. September 9, 1980.

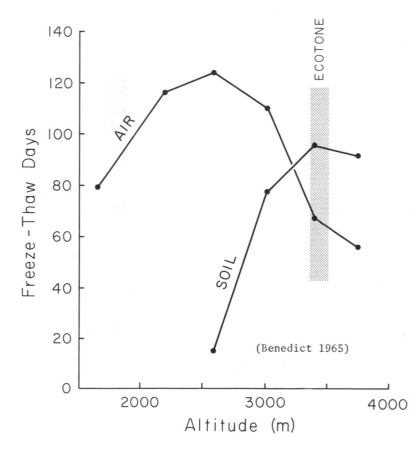

Figure 11. Freeze-thaw along an altitudinal transect on the east slope of the Colorado Front Range, August 1, 1963 to July 31, 1964. A "freeze-thaw day" is a day on which the maximum temperature exceeds 0°C and the minimum temperature is less than 0°C. Air temperatures were measured in Weather Bureau-type instrument shelters; soil temperatures were measured at 2.5-cm depth in bare, sandy, standard soils. If bare *rock* surfaces are analogous to bare *soil* surfaces, granular disintegration due to freezing and thawing should reach a maximum in the timberline ecotone.

Measurements made in the study area (Fig. 9e) illustrate the kinds of problems associated with the use of differential weathering in relative-age dating. The data show an interesting bimodality, but one that is not easily attributed to differences in deposit age. Boulders on three of the youngest deposits, for example, are pitted and etched as deeply as boulders on late Pinedale till, despite a 4- to 5-fold age difference. Shallow depths of differential weathering on outwash terraces are due, in part, to the scarcity of large boulders on these deposits and to the initial resistance to pitting of stones with stream-smoothed surfaces. Shallow depths on three rock glaciers reflect the unexplained failure of *gneisses* to become deeply etched; *granitic* boulders are pitted more deeply on these deposits (2.6-2.7 cm) than on other rock-glacier lobes (2.0-2.1 cm).

Etching of gneisses was deeper than pitting of granites at 12 of 17 localities. This is attributed to the relative resistance of biotite-rich layers in the gneiss, which weather more slowly than the ridges between weathering pits in granite, and provide relatively stable reference surfaces for measurement. Lithologic factors such as the spacing of biotite-rich layers strongly influence potential depths of differential weathering (Fig. 8).

Weathering-Rind Thickness. Weathering rinds are rims of altered rock that form as cobbles weather. Rind thicknesses have been used for relative dating in many parts of the Southern and Central Rocky Mountains (R. Nelson 1954, Birkeland 1973, Carroll 1974, C. Miller and Birkeland 1974, Madole 1976b, Shroba 1977). Most previous studies have involved medium- and coarse-textured igneous rock types such as granite, which are susceptible to spalling and pitting. Such rock types do not give satisfactory results at high altitudes because their surfaces commonly disintegrate more rapidly than rinds can develop (Birkeland 1973).

Fine-textured rock types are better-suited for weathering-rind studies because of their resistance to granular disintegration. Well-preserved glacial striations show that the original surfaces of fine-grained and aphanitic Tertiary dike rocks can survive for tens of thousands of years on Front Range moraines without appreciable spalling. First-generation weathering rinds, a rarity in granites and granodiorites, are commonplace in cobbles and boulders of rock types such as fine-grained quartz diorite, augite latite, and hornblende latite.

Weathering of fine-textured and aphanitic cobbles produces sharply-defined zones of alteration (Fig. 12). Measurements in the Diamond Lake drainage, south of the Fourth of July valley (Fig. 2), suggest that a consistent relationship exists between rind thickness and relative age in deposits at least as old as 10,000 years. Unfortunately, source dikes are irregularly distributed in the Indian Peaks, and boulders of these rock types are rapidly reduced in size during glacial transport. Within the study area, only quartz diorite (classification of Streckeisen 1976) is present. Cobbles and boulders of this rock type occur on outwash terraces and moraines (Fig. 9f), but not on other deposits; their mineralogy and

Figure 12. Weathering-rind development in a quartz latite cobble. The sharply-defined zone of alteration is about 4 mm thick, slightly below average for the late Satanta Peak terminal moraine (SPm2) on which the cobble was collected.

distribution suggest derivation from a single source, now buried beneath surficial debris.

Rates of weathering-rind formation are influenced by differences in mineralogy[5]. This has not been a factor in the Fourth of July valley study area due to the single-source origin of the quartz diorite, but may result in unsatisfactory correlation with deposits whose boulders are derived from different source dikes. A study of mineralogic variation between dikes, and its effects on chemical weathering, is needed before this factor can be evaluated.

Other possible sources of variation are lichen and snow cover. If weathering-rind development is favored by the presence of lichens, as suggested by Jackson and Keller (1970) for basaltic lavas in Hawaii, and by Colman (1977) for andesites in the West Yellowstone area, rind development should be most rapid in environments where lichen growth is unaffected by periodic intervals of snowbank expansion. Thorn's (1975) observation that weathering rinds are better developed near the center of a persistent snowbank on Niwot Ridge (NE of the study area) than at its margins is not necessarily a contradiction. The rock type studied by Thorn (syenite) is susceptible to granular disintegration; reduced rind thicknesses near the margins of the snowbank may reflect spalling due to more-frequent freeze-thaw alternations.

Whatever their effect, differences in lichen cover and snow accumulation are unlikely to have been a factor in the present study: all weathering-rind measurements were made in areas of post-Audubon lichen cover, which are thought to have experienced generally similar snowbank-expansion and lichen-kill histories.

Because of the complicating effects of lichens, fire, and other factors, Colman (1977) has recommended that weathering rinds be measured on subsurface, rather than surface, stones. This was not feasible in the Fourth of July valley study area because of the scarcity of quartz diorite cobbles.

Colman (1977) has also recommended the use of *mean*, rather than *maximum*, weathering-rind thicknesses for comparing deposits. This is appropriate when dealing with undisturbed moraines. However, where slumping or other kinds of disturbance have occurred (as, for example, on the early Satanta Peak lateral moraine in the study area, and on several reactivated rock glaciers in the Diamond Lake valley), *maximum* thicknesses (Fig. 9f) provide a better basis for comparison.

Interestingly, rates of weathering-rind formation above timberline in the Colorado Rocky Mountains are one to two orders of magnitude greater than rates determined for andesites and basalts in lower-altitude moraine sequences (Crandell and Miller 1974, Porter 1975, Colman 1977, Scott 1977, Pierce 1979).

Rapid rind development is characteristic not only of quartz diorite in the Fourth of July valley, but of fine-grained granodiorite on Mount Sopris (Birkeland 1973), and of hornblende latite and augite latite in the Diamond Lake drainage. Faster weathering of these rock types than of andesite and basalt cannot be easily attributed to mineralogical differences or to differences in grain size; more probably it is related to climatic and biological factors that cause chemical weathering to proceed at an accelerated pace in the local timberline environment.

Soil-Profile Development. Differences in soil-profile development have been used as a measure of relative age at a number of Rocky Mountain localities (R. Nelson 1954, Birkeland 1973, Benedict 1973a, Mahaney 1973a, C. Miller and Birkeland 1974, Oviatt 1977, Shroba 1977, 1978, among others). One reason for their popularity is that soil properties such as B-horizon thickness and intensity of oxidation continue to evolve long after many other relative-dating criteria have reached steady-state equilibria. According to Birkeland *et al.* (1979b), soils can be used to differentiate glacial deposits ranging in age from late Holocene to several hundred thousand years.

Soil-profile characteristics were studied at localities chosen to minimize the effects of soil-forming factors other than age (Fig. 13)[6]. Profiles were described beneath tundra vegetation in level to gently-sloping terrain, where erosion and deposition are not currently important. All but four of the profile pits were dug in well-drained, convex ridgetops; the exceptions (localities 1, 4, 5, and 6) were dug in till-covered benches or outwash terraces that receive groundwater seepage during the early-summer snowmelt period. Parent materials are chemically similar at all localities.

Soil texture (hydrometer), gravel content (sieving), organic-matter content (weight loss on ignition), and pH (saturated paste) were determined by James R. Rogers, Front Range Labs, Inc., Fort Collins. Textural class names follow the U.S.D.A. *Soil Survey Manual* (Soil Survey Staff 1951); colors are from *Munsell Soil Color Charts* (Munsell Color Company, Inc. 1954); horizon nomenclature follows Birkeland (1974).

Because soil-profile development cannot begin in a rock glacier until loess or other fine material has accumulated in the interstices between boulders, rock glaciers cannot be satisfactorily compared with moraines or with other rock glaciers on the basis of soils.

Al-Horizon Thickness. Archeological excavations such as those reported in chapters 3 and 4 show that the 0 and A1 horizons of many Front Range morainal soils are substantially younger

---

[5] *A discouraging number of weathering-rind studies fail to identify the rock types involved.*

[6] *Profiles from the intersections of N-S and E-W baselines at excavated archeological sites are included in the summaries (Fig. 9).*

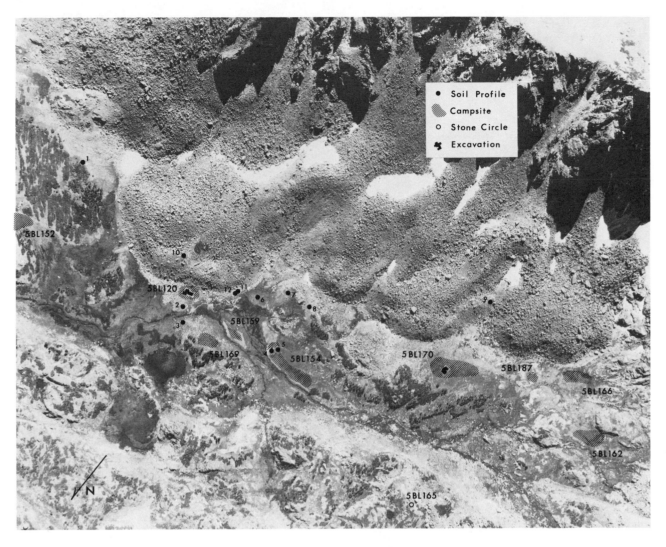

Figure 13. Air-photo map showing the locations of soil-profile pits and archeological sites in the Fourth of July valley study area.

than underlying till. The reason is that they are developed in loess or reworked loess, which is fragile and easily eroded because of its fine texture. An extreme example is at the Caribou Lake site (5 GA 22), where the modern A1 horizon of a Satanta Peak moraine known to be older than 9915 ± 165 radiocarbon years (I-6335) is developed in loess that was deposited at the site less than 765 ± 90 radiocarbon years ago (I-5450).

In the Fourth of July valley study area, the thicknesses of 0 and A1 horizons are variable and inconsistent, reaching maximum values on the youngest rock glacier (Fig. 9h); organic-matter content gives similarly misleading results.

B-Horizon Thickness. B horizons are developed at least partially in coarse-textured sediments, are less vulnerable to erosion than A1 horizons, and are potentially more useful for relative dating. Only cambic B horizons (Soil Survey Staff 1975), distinguished from unal-

tered parent material by their 10YR, 7.5YR, and 5YR hues, were encountered in the study area. The base of the B horizon was taken as the depth at which moist Munsell hue changes to 2.5Y or 5Y. This is commonly a gradual and subtle transition, perception of which varies from individual to individual, and with differences in lighting and soil moisture; less commonly the transition is abrupt, occurring at a permeability barrier, and marked by an accumulation of ferric iron oxide or translocated humus (Fig. 24).

Within the study area, B-horizon thicknesses decrease from a maximum of 55 cm, in late Pinedale ground moraine, to a minimum of 0 cm, in mudflow or avalanche debris and loess at the surface of a late Triple Lakes lobate rock glacier. Despite an overall tendency for B horizons to thicken with time, this criterion does not have the resolution required to distinguish between deposits of closely similar age (Fig. 9i). Like other criteria related to soil-profile development, its value is limited by variation within individual deposits, and by the fact that it is generally impractical to dig enough soil pits to assess that variation.

Strength of Oxidation. Redness and chroma are governed by the strength and color of iron coatings on mineral grains. They are affected by the mineralogy of the deposit, the rate at which iron is released in weathering (a function of climatic and biological variables), the thickness of the zone in which iron compounds are precipitated, the kinds of secondary iron compounds formed, the surface areas of mineral particles in the zone of iron accumulation, the masking effects of soil humus, and other factors — one of which is *time*. As with weathering-pit development, the effects of time can be obscured by environmental factors that vary with elevation. In the Indian Peaks region, oxidation becomes stronger with deposit age only above timberline and in the upper subalpine forest. Oxidation colors are seldom as well developed at lower altitudes as they are near timberline, even in deposits of much greater antiquity[7].

Oxidation was evaluated using an index based on the "color development equivalents" of Buntley and Westin (1965). Beginning with the moist Munsell notation of each horizon, I assigned a numerical value to hue (5Y=1, 2.5Y=2, 10YR=3, 7.5YR=4, etc.), multiplied this number by chroma, adjusted for mottling (if present), and multiplied by horizon thickness in centimeters. For example, a 10-cm-thick B horizon with a 10YR 4/6 m color received an index number of 180. A 20-cm-thick 10YR 4/3 m horizon in which 7.5YR 4/8 m mottles accounted for *ca.* 5% of total volume received an index number of 203. Index numbers were summed for the entire profile above the Cox horizon, which could not be included because its thickness was unknown. Results (Fig. 9j) do little more than quantify the obvious: (1) rock-glacier soils are weakly oxidized relative to morainal soils, and (2) differences in strength of oxidation do not provide the resolution needed to distinguish between the study-area moraines. Other color indices (Harden and Marchand 1977, Hurst 1977) were tried without improved results.

Depth of Loess Infiltration. The presence and thickness of windblown silt (loess) has been used as an indicator of relative age in several western mountain ranges (Birkeland 1973, C. Miller and Birkeland 1974, Shroba 1978). Its value in the Indian Peaks is questionable, in part because loess units are so frequently recycled, and in part because horizontal variability within deposits is so great.

It is virtually impossible to find undisturbed loess above timberline in the Indian Peaks. Most high-altitude loess deposits have

been reworked by frost-sorting and slopewash processes, causing incorporation of sand and gravel. Vertical frost sorting (Corte 1963) has caused downward migration of loess throughout the layer of soil affected by seasonal freezing and thawing, as indicated by silt caps on stones more than a meter below ground surface. In figure 9k I have plotted the depth to the base of the lowest horizon in which the dry weight of particles finer than 0.05 mm (silt and clay) exceeds the dry weight of particles coarser than 2.0 mm (gravel). This corresponds, in most instances, to the lowest horizon recognized in the field as having an important loess component.

Archeological excavations on moraines above timberline illustrate the horizontal variability of loess infiltration (for example, see stratigraphic profiles in chapters 3 and 4). Differences in exposure to erosion by wind and running water, small differences in surface topography that existed at the time of loess deposition, and local differences in the frost-disturbance histories of the deposits all play a role. Thus it is not surprising that no clear-cut relationship exists between loess infiltration and relative age in the Fourth of July valley study area (Fig. 9k).

Number of Soil Horizons. Figure 9l shows the number of identifiable soil horizons (excluding archeological horizons and facies of the original parent material) above the Cox horizon. This is a measure of the strength and nature of pedogenesis, the number of depositional processes that have affected the profile locality, and the degree to which depositional units have been modified by processes such as frost sorting, all of which can be expected to increase with the exposure age of a moraine or rock glacier.

Local factors can cause variations in profile complexity within short distances, and different observers can record different sequences of soil horizons in a single exposure. A tendency for soil profiles to become increasingly complex with age exists in the Fourth of July valley study area (Fig. 9l), but does not provide the resolution needed to distinguish between deposits.

Evaluation. As emphasized by Birkeland *et al.* (1979b), no glacial chronology can be more detailed than the resolution of the dating criteria used. In the Fourth of July valley timberline ecotone — where variables other than time (i.e., altitude, rock type, snow cover, macroclimate, vegetation, etc.) are as uniform as are likely to be encountered in a study of alpine glacial deposits — weathering rind thicknesses in fine-textured igneous rocks are the only relative-dating criterion with the resolution required for subdividing deposits of late Pinedale to Triple Lakes age (*ca.* 14,000 to 3000 ^{14}C yr) into stadial-rank units. Unfortunately, fine-textured Tertiary dike rocks are uncommon in the Indian Peaks, and are absent in many valleys; coarse-textured rock types are ubiquitous, but give unsatisfactory results due to their susceptibility to

---

[7] *A similar altitudinal relationship has been reported in the Sierra Nevada of California (Birkeland* et al. *1979a).*

granular disintegration. Mineralogical differences between dikes may complicate valley-to-valley correlation. The effects of altitude, snow cover, and lichen cover on weathering-rind development remain to be evaluated.

Criteria related to B-horizon thickness, strength of profile oxidation, and number of soil horizons show gross changes within this time interval, but lack the resolution that weathering rinds are capable of providing. They suggest that a significant age difference exists between rock glaciers and moraines in the study area (Fig. 9i, j, 1); however, the soils on rock glaciers are in deposits that may be thousands of years younger than the rock glaciers themselves, and therefore are irrelevant. A greater number of environmental factors affect soils than affect weathering rinds, making soils the more difficult to interpret. Furthermore, and most problematical, the variability observed in short horizontal distances at archeological sites on moraines suggests that data from a single profile pit cannot be considered representative; the time, labor, and aesthetic damage involved in *adequately* sampling a moraine are prohibitively large.

Several criteria tested (vascular plant cover, percent lichen cover, percent weathered granitic boulders) cannot be used for differentiating deposits as old as those in the study area because they have already reached maximum development. Each, however, can be used for dating moraines and rock glaciers younger than about 3000 yr. The effective dating range of surface granite weathering could be doubled or perhaps tripled by modifying the measurement technique as suggested in footnote 4.

The remaining criteria (boulder frequency, depth of differential weathering, distal slope angles of moraines, rock-glacier front angles, degree of stream dissection) are influenced so strongly by the initial character of the deposit and/or environmental factors that the time element can seldom be satisfactorily isolated.

LICHENOMETRY

Introduction. *Rhizocarpon geographicum* s.l. is a crustose lichen of worldwide distribution and slow growth; it has the longest lifespan of any known living organism (Benedict 1967, G. Miller and Andrews 1972). Its growth rate has been measured in environments as diverse as the St. Elias Mountains (Denton and Karlén 1977), the Brooks Range (Calkin and Ellis 1980), the Southern Alps of New Zealand (Burrows and Orwin 1971), the Cascade Range (Porter 1981), the Sierra Nevada (Curry 1969), Baffin Island (Andrews and Barnett 1979), the Canadian Rockies (Luckman 1977), Swedish Lapland (Karlen 1973), West Greenland (Ten Brink 1973), and the maritime Antarctic (Lindsay 1973). Growth rates vary from region to region,

being slowest in cold, continental environments with short growing seasons (Webber and Andrews 1973). Where the relationship between thallus diameter and age can be established, maximum-diameter *R. geographicum* s.l. thalli can be used for dating moraines and rock glaciers.

More than four decades ago, E.B. Renaud (1939) outlined a method for dating prehistoric quartzite quarry tools based on the time required for colonization by different species of crustose and foliose lichens. The origins of modern lichenometry, however, can be traced to the pioneering studies of Roland Beschel (1950, 1956, 1958a, 1958b, 1961). Only during the past 10-15 years has the method come into widespread use among glacial geologists. Most applications have involved maximum-diameter measurements of *R. geographicum* s.l. in high-altitude or high-latitude environments. Archeological applications include those of Follmann (1961, 1965), who used lichenometry to date statues on Easter Island, and Kvamme (1977), who tried unsuccessfully to use it for dating prehistoric quarries in northeastern Colorado.

Lichen Growth on Historic Control Surfaces. The time required for colonization of stable substrates by *R. geographicum* s.l., and the growth rate of the species during its first century of life, under optimum microclimatic conditions, are estimated in figure 14B. Estimates are based upon maximum-diameter lichen measurements made on stable surfaces of known historic age. The surfaces include cemetery markers in the high-altitude mining camps of Caribou and Central City, dams and quarry walls in the Boulder City Watershed, railroad cuts and tunnel tailings on Rollins Pass, cairns built during a topographic survey of the Indian Peaks, and highway cuts along Trail Ridge Road. Only the localities most critical to construction of the growth curve (marked *A*, *B*, *C*, and *D* in figure 14B) are described below.

Point A. A 4-mm *R. geographicum* s.l. thallus was measured in 1966 on the riprap facing of a dam at Green Lake No. 1, Boulder City Watershed. The altitude of the reservoir is 3430 m. Boulders used to face the dam were quarried from a nearby moraine in 1937; rock types include biotite gneiss, monzonite, quartz monzonite, and biotite latite. Some of the rocks retain their pre-construction lichen covers; measurements were restricted to the fresh faces of boulders that showed definite trimlines. The largest *R. geographicum* s.l. thallus grew on the NW-facing surface of a boulder in a locality that receives spray from the reservoir on windy days in summer and fall; lichen growth is likely to have been especially rapid here because of the favorable moisture regime.

Point B. Construction of Trail Ridge Road, Rocky Mountain National Park, was begun in 1929 and completed in 1932. In 1966, an 8-mm *R. geographicum* s.l. thallus was measured on a NNW-facing exposure of Precambrian biotite gneiss in a road cut near Rainbow Curve, altitude 3370 m. A second thallus of the same diameter was

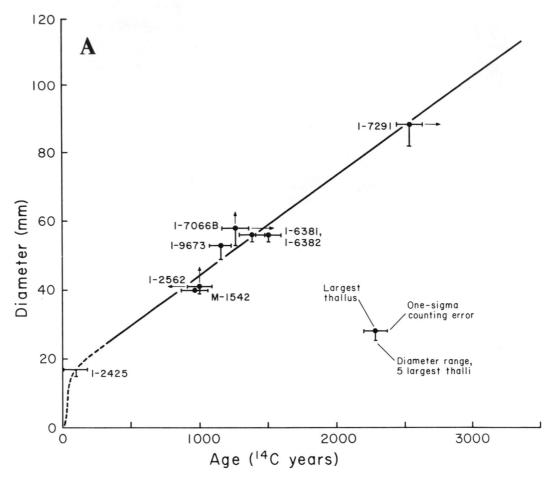

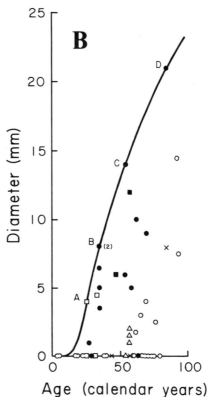

Figure 14. Growth-rate curves for *Rhizocarpon geographicum* s.l., Indian Peaks region, Colorado Front Range. <u>A</u>, long-term growth rate, based on radiocarbon-dated control surfaces; arrows indicate the directions that control points would probably be displaced if it were possible to correct for inherent errors. <u>B</u>, initial growth rate, based on historically-dated surfaces; the curve is for optimum (i.e., stable, moist) conditions.

measured on a SSW-facing exposure of biotite gneiss at Rock Cut, altitude 3705 m. Neither locality is unusually moist; both, however, experience artificially-long growing seasons because Trail Ridge Road is opened by snow-plows in May.

Point C. A 14-mm *R. geographicum* s.l. thallus was recorded in 1966 on the W-facing wall of a quarry in granodiorite south of the dam at Silver Lake, Boulder City Watershed. The quarry is at an altitude of 3125 m, and was dug for construction material during the winter of 1911-1912. Its W- and NW-facing walls are steep and shaded, and provide an unusually moist (i.e., favorable) micro-environment for lichen growth (Benedict 1967, Table 1).

Point D. A 21-mm *R. geographicum* s.l. thallus was measured in 1966 on biotite gneiss at the entrance to a tunnel north of Yankee Doodle Lake, elevation 3275 m. The tunnel dates from 1882, when an abortive attempt was made by the Denver, Utah, & Pacific Railroad to drive a bore from this location into the Middle Boulder Creek basin, enroute to western Colorado (Black 1969). The 21-mm thallus grew in a crevice in the moist and shaded NW-facing wall of a trench at the tunnel entrance; no other *R. geographicum* s.l. thalli larger than 15 mm were noted at the tunnel locality.

Lichen Growth on Radiocarbon-Dated Control Surfaces. The long-term growth rate of the species (Fig. 14A) was estimated by measuring the maximum diameter of the largest circular or nearly-circular *R. geographicum* s.l. thallus growing on each of 7 radiocarbon-dated control surfaces believed to be environmentally similar to moraines and rock glaciers in the Indian Peaks region. The control surfaces include mudflow levees and alluvial fans, a prehistoric game drive, a rock glacier, and an area of Audubon-age lichen kill. Two of three surfaces used in constructing a preliminary growth-rate curve (Benedict 1967) are retained; the third is omitted here because of doubts concerning its interpretation.

Mudflow Levees, Arapaho Cirque. The youngest radiocarbon-dated control point used in the original growth-rate curve is from Arapaho Cirque, where a date of <180 yr BP (I-2425) was obtained for the upper 1 mm of a IIA1b horizon buried beneath mudflow levees at an altitude of 3500 m. Size-frequency analysis of the *R. geographicum* s.l. community growing on the levees showed that no lichens had survived the flow; the fastest-growing *R. geographicum* s.l. colonist was 17 mm in maximum dimension. Details concerning the size structure of the lichen population can be found in Benedict (1967: 823-826).

Game-Drive Wall, Mount Albion. Another of the original control points was obtained from archeological site 5 BL 65 (Benedict 1975a),

a game-drive site on the upper slopes of Mount Albion, 3660 m above sea level. Size-frequency analysis was used to divide a sample of 2000 *R. geographicum* s.l. thalli growing on a stone drive wall at the site into two groups: (1) survivors of wall building, and (2) colonists of rock surfaces that were freshly exposed by wall construction. Details are in Benedict (1967: 826-829). Results suggest that a thallus diameter of 40 mm can be equated with a radiocarbon age of 970 ± 100 yr (M-1542), the age of charcoal associated with small corner-notched projectile points in one of 16 rock-walled pits related to the drive system.

Arapaho Rock Glacier. During the summer of 1966, erosion by a meltwater stream exposed a 220-m-long section of buried glacial ice in the Arapaho rock glacier (Benedict 1973b). A date of 1000 ± 90 BP (I-2562) was obtained for pollen, spruce and fir twigs and needles, cushion-plant fragments (cf. *Silene acaulis*), unidentified plant fragments, and insect remains from an ablation surface 310 m from the cirque headwall, at an altitude of 3680 m (Fig. 15). Lichens were measured on bouldery debris above the ice. It was difficult to be certain how large an area should be sampled: *R. geographicum* s.l. thalli growing on large, stable boulders in the *immediate* vicinity of the radiocarbon locality had diameters as large as 41 mm, whereas lichens in a somewhat broader area reached diameters as large as 49 mm. In figure 14A I have plotted the 41 mm diameter, treating it as a minimum value. Because the debris cover of the rock glacier is younger than the ice beneath it, and must originally have been too unstable for lichen colonization, the largest *R. geographicum* s.l. thallus growing on the rock glacier at the radiocarbon locality is likely to be several hundred years younger than the age of underlying ice.

Mudflow Levee, Upper Diamond Lake Valley. In 1976 I measured lichens on a bouldery mudflow levee 50 m east of the outlet of Upper Diamond Lake, 3580 m above sea level. The largest clearly-defined *R. geographicum* s.l. thallus was 53 mm in maximum diameter; the age of the mudflow is believed to be 1155 ± 85 radiocarbon years (I-9673), based on a date for the NaOH-soluble, HCl-insoluble fraction of soil humus from a IIA1b horizon developed in till and buried by the levee (Fig. 16). No correction was made for the mean residence time of carbon in the buried soil because only the uppermost 5 mm of the IIA1b horizon — believed to consist of the remains of plants that died as a result of burial — was dated. Contamination by modern rootlets, which penetrate deeply into the mudflow deposit and buried soil, is the probable reason that the NaOH-insoluble fraction of the sample gave a radiocarbon age of 945 ± 85 yr (I-9672). The older date is believed to be most reliable, and is used in figure 14A.

Figure 15. Glacial ice in the core of Arapaho rock glacier. Lichens were measured on boulders directly above the ice, which had a radiocarbon age of 1000 ± 90 yr at this locality. September 11, 1966.

Figure 16. Buried soil beneath mudflow levee, Upper Diamond Lake valley. Mudflow debris overlies glacial till. A ^{14}C date of 1155 ± 85 BP for the upper 5 mm of the IIA1b horizon dates the flow. August 19, 1976.

Figure 17. Bog in Caribou Lake valley. A pack marks the ^{14}C-sampling locality. Lichens were measured between bog and trees, on till of Satanta Peak age. Caribou Lake is hidden behind the moraine; the north buttress of Mount Neva is in the background. September 23, 1973.

Figure 18. Henderson alluvial fan. Fan deposits of Audubon (A$_1$, A$_2$) and late Triple Lakes (TL) age overlie Triple Lakes lateral moraine at type locality, Arapaho Cirque. The age of the moraine is disputed. Dot marks location of ^{14}C samples. September 22, 1973.

Caribou Lake Valley. Much of the upper part of the Caribou Lake valley was covered with late-lying snow during Audubon time, destroying the pre-existing lichen cover. Included in the area affected by Audubon-age lichen kill is a kettle-hole depression in till southeast of the lake outlet, 3410 m above sea level. Here trimlines on large boulders indicate destruction of the lichen cover to a height 1.5-1.8 m above the modern ground surface.

A pit dug in muck and sedge peat on the floor of the depression exposed a thin layer of greenish gray (5GY 6/1 m) micaceous silt loam, 28-29 cm below the surface of the bog; coring demonstrated that the deposit coarsened in the direction of a low till ridge upslope from the bog (Fig. 17). I interpret the silt layer as a slopewash deposit, formed when the floor of the valley was emerging from beneath a blanket of perennial snow or was seasonally snow-covered for much of the summer. Either condition would have weakened the vegetation cover of the moraine, favoring erosion and redeposition of fine-textured clastic sediments.

The age of the clastic layer is indicated by radiocarbon dates of 1505 ± 95 BP (I-6382, NaOH-insoluble) and 1390 ± 95 BP (I-6381, NaOH-insoluble), for 1-cm-thick muck samples collected directly below and above it. The dates provide an approximation of the time available for lichen recolonization of the moraine that was the source of the clastic sediments. They are equated with a maximum *R. geographicum* s.l. diameter of 56 mm, measured in 1973 on till directly upslope from the bog (Fig. 17).

Henderson Alluvial Fan. The Henderson Glacier occupies a cirque at the head of a hanging valley in the Boulder City Watershed. Debris from the mouth of the valley forms an alluvial fan that overlies till at the Triple Lakes type locality, downvalley from Arapaho Glacier (Fig. 18). The fan consists of three superimposed lobes, which terminate in a moraine-dammed lake approximately 3470 m above sea level. The youngest lobe (A_2), which has a post-Audubon lichen cover, is graded to the present level of the lake. The second-youngest lobe (A_1), also of Audubon age, is graded to a lake level slightly higher than the present, and is truncated by erosion at the modern shoreline. The oldest lobe (TL), which has a post-Triple Lakes lichen cover and weathering characteristics, was in existence when water in the lake stood 1.4 m higher than its present level, as indicated by a high strandline on this portion of the composite fan. Each lobe of the fan is believed to record a time of high sediment production related to glacial activity in the Henderson Cirque.

A profile pit dug near the toe of the older Audubon lobe (Fig. 18) penetrated 20-26 cm of soil humus and interbedded eolian sand layers; 65-73 cm of Audubon-age fan material; 24-31 cm of late Triple Lakes fan material;

proglacial lake sediments with a radiocarbon age of 3865 ± 100 yr (I-6986); and till of the inner Triple Lakes moraine. Soils were developed in both of the fan deposits. A date of 2540 ± 95 BP (I-7291, NaOH-insoluble) was obtained for the full 5-cm thickness of a IIIA1b horizon in the late Triple Lakes fan. Dates of 1220 ± 135 BP (I-7066A, NaOH-soluble, HCl-insoluble) and 1270 ± 100 BP (I-7066B, NaOH-insoluble) were obtained for the basal 2 cm of a 14-cm-thick IIA1b horizon developed in Audubon-age fan material.

Lichens were measured on the alluvial fans in 1973. If (as seems probable) lichen growth on the deposits began simultaneously with soil development, a *R. geographicum* s.l. diameter of 58 mm can be equated with a soil that began to form sometime prior to *ca.* 1270 radiocarbon yr BP, and a diameter of 88 mm can be equated with a soil that began to form prior to 2540 radiocarbon yr BP. Potential sources of error are numerous. They include (1) penetration of the younger soil by modern rootlets[8], (2) uncertainty concerning the extent to which the radiocarbon dates underestimate the time of inception of soil formation, (3) difficulties inherent in dating soil organic matter (Goh *et al.* 1977, Gilet-Blein *et al.* 1980), and (4) the limited number and diversity of habitats available for lichen growth on the older Audubon deposit. As a result, neither of these two control points is considered to be particularly reliable.

<u>Interpretation of the Growth-Rate Curves.</u> The time required for colonization of stable, favorably-oriented rock surfaces by *R. geographicum* s.l. is estimated from figure 14B to be 20-30 years. Longer lag times can be anticipated on deposits that are initially unstable, or are xeric, or are composed of boulders whose surfaces are smooth and polished.

Growth rates during the first century of exposure approach 20-25 mm/100 yr in moist microenvironments such as localities *A*, *B*, *C*, and *D* (Fig. 14B), and about 15 mm/100 yr in drier microenvironments. The latter are more characteristic of moraines and rock glaciers in the region. These values are low in comparison with the growth rate of 30 mm/100 yr measured on tombstones at Silverton, in the San Juan Mountains (Carrara and Andrews 1973). Much of the scatter in figure 14B is due to the inclusion of data from cairns and cemetery markers, whose small sizes limit their individual usefulness as control surfaces.

Following a century of rapid growth (Beschel's "great period"), growth rates decline to an average rate of about 2.9 mm/100 ^{14}C yr. This portion of the curve is drawn as a straight line, but may eventually prove to have a different shape (Porter 1981). Analysis of potential errors (Fig. 14A) indicates that future modifi-

---

[3] *Close agreement between dates for the NaOH-soluble and NaOH-insoluble fractions of the sample suggests that the effects of rootlet contamination are not large.*

cations to the curve are likely to involve extension of the "great period" and a lower rate of growth during the "linear" phase.

Sources of Error. It is not yet possible to give quantitative estimates of the errors involved in lichenometric dating. Errors associated with construction of the growth curve will be compounded by errors resulting from its misapplication. Examples of the latter include (1) failure to recognize complex thalli, composed of more than a single individual, (2) attempting to date deposits that are too small or too overgrown by vegetation to provide optimum lichen habitats, (3) failure to recognize lichen survivors on boulders that have fallen, rolled, or been carried by avalanches from nearby cliffs, (4) attempting to date deposits that are environmentally different from the surfaces on which the growth curve was established, (5) failure to take into account variations in colonization time related to rock texture and stability of substrate, and (6) failure to recognize areas of snow kill, fire, or other disturbance. Given these and other difficulties, it would be a mistake to expect great precision from the method.

Because of the nature of the radiocarbon-dated surfaces used in constructing the growth-rate curve, use of the curve should be restricted to areas above present timberline in the Front Range, where deposits composed of granitic or gneissic rock types occur in well-drained sites that are snow-free for much of the summer.

Applications of Lichenometry in the Fourth of July Valley. The maximum diameters of circular and nearly-circular R. geographicum s.l. thalli were measured on all map units in the study area. Results are summarized in figure 19. Lichen diameters cannot be used to date deposits as old as Satanta Peak and Ptarmigan moraines. However, they provide minimum ages (perhaps *close* minimum ages) for late Triple Lakes rock glaciers along the base of the N-facing valley wall.

The tendency for lichens to be killed and removed from their substrates by late-lying snow was the basis for a second application of the method. Large sectors of the valley floor (including an estimated 90-95% of the study area) are characterized by low percent lichen cover, undersized R. geographicum s.l. thalli, and a high proportion of successional species such as Lecanora thomsonii and Lecidea atrobrunnea. Such communities are believed to have become established following a period of expanded snow cover during Audubon time[9]. Maximum R. geographicum s.l. diameters of 61 to 71 mm (Fig. 19) indicate that recolonization of knolls and ridgecrests began 1600 to 1900 radiocarbon years ago; smaller maximum diameters indicate that depressions and sheltered areas remained snow-covered for hundreds of years longer.

[9] *The hypothesis that lichen destruction was the result of an expanded forest cover, loess accumulation, or fire was rejected because areas of openwork rubble — unlikely to have been tree covered or to have accumulated important thicknesses of windblown silt — were affected as markedly as areas of finer textured soil.*

Figure 19. Maximum R. *geographicum* s.l. diameters, Fourth of July valley study area. Lichen diameters can be converted to minimum ages using the growth-rate curve in figure 14A.

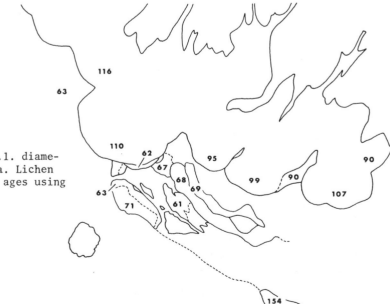

To determine the duration of snow cover required to destroy a lichen community, lines of lichen-covered stones were placed on the floors of two late-lying snowbanks in the Fourth of July valley; the condition of the lichens and the positions of the snowbank margins were monitored beginning in 1974. Preliminary results suggest that (1) the lichen-free zones associated with modern snowbanks are in equilibrium with present-day conditions, rather than relicts of 18th or 19th century snowbank expansion; (2) *R. geographicum* s.l. is slightly less vulnerable to snow kill than other lichen species studied (*Lecanora thomsonii*, *Lecidea atrobrunnea*, *Caloplaca elegans*, *Umbilicaria virginis*); and (3) the boundary between healthy *R. geographicum* s.l. thalli and thalli that have begun to discolor and spall after six seasons on the floor of a late-lying snowbank corresponds to an average melt-out date of July 25th, and an average annual snow-free season of 85 days (*ca.* 12 weeks). Extreme, rather than average, conditions may be responsible for lichen mortality; however, *R. geographicum* s.l. thalli clearly require a longer snow-free growing period than the 4-6 weeks previously suspected (Benedict 1967).

ARCHEOLOGICAL DATING

Many opportunities for archeological dating exist in the Fourth of July valley. Within the study area alone there are nine known campsites and a circular stone enclosure of prehistoric human origin (Fig. 13). Eight of the sites are younger than the outermost moraine, and at least one site is younger than the innermost. Two of the sites have been excavated (Chapters 3 and 4), providing cultural material and datable charcoal.

Minimum ages can in some cases be estimated from artifact styles found on the surface. Projectile points are particularly useful for this purpose because of stylistic changes through time. Projectile points collected in the study area are illustrated in figure 20, together with their approximate ages, where these can be estimated from radiocarbon dates associated with similar artifacts found elsewhere.

RADIOCARBON DATING

Twenty-one samples from the study area were analyzed by James D. Buckley, Teledyne Isotopes, producing a total of 33 individual radiocarbon dates. The samples include charcoal, muck, peat, soil humus, and lake silts. Ages were calculated using a half-life of 5568 ± 30 years, and are reported in radiocarbon years BP (years before 1950), without correction for secular $^{14}C/^{12}C$ variations or isotopic fractionation. Errors (± 1σ) include standard deviations for sample counts, background, and modern standard.

The radiocarbon method and its limitations are subjects much too large to address here. Ogden (1977) and Stuckenrath (1977) have prepared excellent review papers; a wealth of information can be found in the *Proceedings* of the Twelfth Nobel Symposium (Olsson, *ed.* 1970) and the *Proceedings* of the Eighth, Ninth, and Tenth International Radiocarbon Conferences (Rafter and Grant-Taylor, *eds.* 1972; Berger and Suess, *eds.* 1979; Stuiver and Kra, *eds.* 1980). Potential sources of error unique to the alpine environment or otherwise particularly important to the present study are mentioned below.

In Situ Production of ^{14}C in High-Altitude Wood. Carbon-14 is produced when ^{14}N is bombarded by slow, or thermal, neutrons. We generally think of this process as occurring in the upper atmosphere, where nitrogen is abundant. However, neutron bombardment can also cause *in situ* production of ^{14}C from ^{14}N in the cells of wood and bone. If this were a quantitatively-important process, it might cause dates for high-altitude wood and wood charcoal to be anomalously young. One reason is that the cosmic-ray neutron flux is much greater at high altitudes than at sea level. Another, suggested by L. Libby and Lukens (1973), is that lightning can produce thermal neutrons.

Present evidence indicates that dating errors due to *in situ* production of ^{14}C are unlikely to be large in wood or wood-charcoal samples younger than about 20,000 years (C.J. Radnell, pers. comm. 1980). Harkness and Burleigh (1974) and Radnell *et al.* (1979) were unable to cause significant increases in the ^{14}C activities of pine or oak by neutron irradiation in a reactor. Radnell *et al.* (1979) concluded that the wood did not contain enough ^{14}N for the process to be significant. Experiments with simulated and natural lightning strikes suggest that too few neutrons are produced during a discharge to have an important effect on radiocarbon dating, even for samples collected from high, isolated mountains in regions of frequent thunderstorms (Fleischer *et al.* 1974, Fleischer 1975).

Ages of Trees at Upper Tree Limit. A second potential source of error in dates for high-altitude wood and wood charcoal arises from the ages of living trees at upper tree limit, and their resistance to decay. Although spruce, fir, and limber pine trees above timberline in the Indian Peaks do not have the extreme longevity of bristlecone pines in the mountains of eastern California and Nevada (Currey 1965), they are nevertheless old; a fire built with wood fragments gathered *selectively* from the trails of dead wood left by migrating tree islands (Marr 1977) might conceivably produce charcoal with an initial age of 500-1000 years. Errors of this magnitude are unlikely to have affected dates from the study area: (1) old wood in a prehistoric campfire would almost certainly be mixed with younger twigs and branches; and (2) the study area is in the lower part of the timberline ecotone, where trees have shorter life spans and produce wood that is less dense and

Figure 20. Projectile points from surface collections in the Fourth of July valley study area. *a-b*, site 5 BL 152; *c-d*, site 5 BL 154; *e-f*, site 5 BL 166; *g-j*, site 5 BL 162. Site locations are shown in figure 13. Included in the collection are two Mount Albion Corner-notched projectile points (*a*, *j*), dated elsewhere between 5800 and 5350 yr BP (Benedict and Olson 1978), and three Park points (*g-i*), undated in the Colorado mountains (Stewart 1970), but believed to be related to a style used in the Great Basin *ca*. 4000-3000 yr BP. Points *b*, *d*, and *f* are estimated to be older than 5500, 3000, and 2500 radiocarbon years, respectively. Point *e* is attributed to the Hog Back Phase (C. Nelson 1971), for which there are published high-altitude dates of 1260 and 970 yr BP (Benedict 1975*a*).

resistant to decay than at upper tree limit. I estimate the probable error from this source to be less than 100 radiocarbon years.

Rootlet Contamination in Areas of Fallout Concentration. Contamination by modern rootlets can be an important source of error, particularly if the original carbon content of a sample is small (Olsson 1974). A unique dimension is added to this problem on the floors of late-lying Front Range snowpatches, where fallout radionuclides are concentrated many tens of times above atmospheric levels (Osburn 1963, 1966). Contamination by the rootlets of modern plants that have assimilated man-made ^{14}C is the probable reason that one of the radiocarbon dates obtained in this study (I-11,128A) is several thousand years younger than suggested by other evidence (see p. 67-73).

Isotopic Fractionation. A variety of substances was used for radiocarbon dating in the Fourth of July valley. Dates for peat and soil humus generally require only minor corrections for isotopic fractionation to bring them into agreement with dates for terrestrial wood and wood charcoal (Stuiver and Polach 1977, Gulliksen 1980). An important exception occurs where peat- and humus-forming plant species operate on the C_4 carbon-fixation cycle, rather than the C_3 cycle of pine, spruce, and fir trees. C_4 plants discriminate less strongly against the heavy isotopes of carbon than do C_3 plants; as a result, they tend to give radiocarbon ages that are several hundred years too young. Because the C_4 pathway is an adaptation to hot and/or arid conditions (Teeri and Stowe 1976, Stowe and Teeri 1978), and is uncommon at high elevations (Livingstone and Clayton 1980), isotopic fractionation is an unlikely source of dating error in the Fourth of July valley study area.

Isotopic fractionation can be evaluated by measuring $^{13}C/^{12}C$ ratios. This was not done routinely in the present study. The single $\delta^{13}C$

value obtained for peat from the Fourth of July Valley Bog (-25.6 per mil wrt PDB, I-11,653B) is closely similar to the mean value for terrestrial wood, suggesting that peat-forming plants in the bog have not selectively assimilated the heavy isotopes of carbon.

Buried Soils. Buried soils are common in the Indian Peaks due to the instability of slopes and the catastrophic nature of many alpine geomorphic processes. Four of seven radiocarbon-dated control points used in constructing the lichen-growth curve involve buried soil humus. For two of the control points it was important to know when the soils had begun to form; for two others it was important to know when the soils had become buried.

Time of burial can be estimated by dating the full thickness of a buried A1 horizon and correcting the date by subtracting the mean residence time of carbon at time of burial (Benedict 1966). Published estimates of mean residence time in tundra environments range from 50 to 385 years (Østrem 1965, Benedict 1966, Ellis 1979). However, these estimates are based on dates for modern soils, and are likely to seriously underrepresent mean residence times because of contamination by fallout from nuclear testing.

The problem of mean residence time can be avoided by dating a thin layer of humus skimmed from the upper surface of a buried soil. Assuming that the soil has not been truncated by erosion, or otherwise disturbed during burial (Griffey and Ellis 1979), this uppermost material will consist of the remains of plants that were living at time of burial, and will require no correction for mean residence time. This approach was followed in dating both of the mudflow deposits used as control surfaces for the lichen-growth curve (I-2425, I-9673)[10].

There is no satisfactory way to date the *beginning* of soil formation. Dates for bulk A-horizon samples give minimum ages, but it is impossible to be certain how seriously they underestimate *true* ages. Errors can be reduced by dating thin basal samples (as was done with sample I-7066, Henderson alluvial fan), and by dating immature soils that were buried soon after they began to form (hopefully the case with sample I-7291, Henderson alluvial fan). At best, however, such dates remain minima, and should be treated with caution.

Conclusions. Radiocarbon dates for wood charcoal and bog sediments in the study area are unlikely to have been seriously affected by the sources of error outlined above. Dates for soil humus are considerably less reliable. A date for lake sediments from the floor of a late snowpatch (I-11,128A) is rejected completely due to probable contamination by root-

lets containing high concentrations of fallout radionuclides.

The Deposits

LATE PINEDALE GROUND MORAINE (Pgm)

The oldest depositional unit in the study area is ground moraine of late Pinedale age. The deposit resembles a lateral moraine when viewed from the north (Fig. 21); however, rock outcrops at its eastern end show that the feature is actually a bedrock bench with a thin veneer of till. Prospect pits and mine shafts in a similar bench on the opposite side of the valley, near the Fourth of July Mine, expose shallow bedrock at many places beneath till of comparable age.

Clasts in the till are subangular and subrounded, and include a diversity of rock types that outcrop higher in the valley but are absent in cliffs to the south. Striation directions on bedrock outcrops adjoining the deposit (Fig. 7) also indicate an upvalley origin.

The surface of the till is stable and well vegetated. Tree islands of krummholz Engelmann spruce (*Picea engelmannii*) and subalpine fir (*Abies lasiocarpa*) trail to leeward on its 8° to 13° north-facing slope (Fig. 21). The surface of the bench is a snow-accumulation area, without trees.

Most of the deposit has a sparse lichen cover, reflecting snowbank expansion during Audubon time. An exception is the windswept northern margin of the feature, where lichens are maturely developed (Fig. 9a).

Till on the bench is assigned to the late stade of Pinedale Glaciation based on the elevation and character of the nearest terminal moraines lower in the valley. These lie just east of the Fourth of July Campground, at an altitude of 3000-3050 m, and are similar in elevation and general appearance to deposits attributed by Richmond (1960) and Madole (1969) to the final advance of Pinedale ice.

Relative-dating criteria give no indication that late Pinedale and Satanta Peak advances in the valley were separated by a significant interval of weathering or soil formation. Maximum depths of differential weathering (Fig. 9e) are comparable on deposits of both ages. A soil in the late Pinedale deposit (Fig. 22) shows stronger B-horizon development and deeper loess infiltration than soils in Satanta Peak terminal moraines and outwash terraces higher in the valley (Fig. 9i, j, k); differences, however, are slight, and are difficult to evaluate because of meltwater seepage through the till mantle of the bench at profile locality 1 (Fig. 13).

An accumulation of stones and gravel in the IIB1 horizon of the late Pinedale soil (Fig. 22) suggests that an episode of vertical

---

[10] *A paper just received from John A. Matthews (1980) suggests that samples must be extremely thin if appreciable mean residence times are to be avoided.*

Figure 21 (left). Bedrock bench with mantle of late Pinedale ground moraine (Pgm), viewed from the north. Striations on Precambrian biotite gneiss (PЄbg) trend downvalley. Archeological site 5 BL 152 is in the left foreground. Meltwater from a perennial snowbank at the rear of the bench keeps the till moist in early summer. August 27, 1979.

Figure 22 (below). Soil profile in late Pinedale ground moraine, locality 1 (Fig. 13).

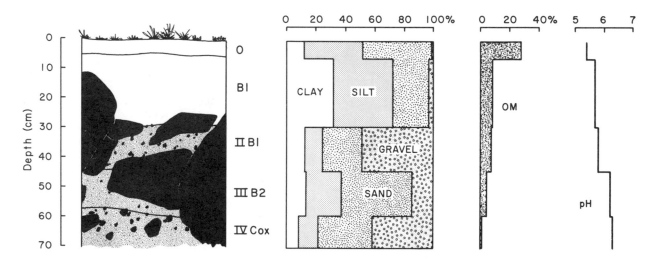

Comment: The profile was described in a tundra clearing at the edge of spruce-fir tree islands. Ground cover included *Vaccinium myrtillus*, *V. scoparium*, *Acomastylis rossii*, *Selaginella densa*, *Deschampsia caespitosa*, *Bistorta bistortoides*, *Polygonum viviparum*, *Pedicularis racemosa*, *Salix arctica*, and *Lepraria arctica*. The profile is less well drained than others examined in this study, due to seepage from late-lying snowbanks at the rear of the bench. The stratigraphic sequence consists of loess and reworked loess above frost-sorted till.

O Very dark brown (10YR 2/3 m) loam. Structureless. Roots abundant.
B1 Dark yellowish brown (10YR 4/3.5 m) clay loam, mottled 10YR 4/6 m. Scattered pebbles and charcoal flecks suggest minor reworking of loess by slopewash; pebbles and coarse sand grains lack colloidal coatings. Strong fine platy structure. Lower boundary an erosion surface.
IIB1 Dark yellowish brown (10YR 3.5/4 m) very stony, gravelly sandy clay loam, mottled 10YR 4/6 m. Structureless. Stoniness is attributed to vertical frost sorting.

IIIB2 Mottled strong brown (7.5YR 4/6 m) and dark yellowish brown (10YR 4/4 m) stony sandy loam. Fine sub-horizontal color banding. Stones have purple stains on lower surfaces, and thin silt-clay caps on upper surfaces. Coarse sand grains and pebbles lack colloidal coatings. Rare fine vesicles.
IVCox Dark grayish brown to olive brown (2.5Y 4/3 m) stony, gravelly sandy loam till. Stones are less numerous than in two overlying horizons, suggesting ejection by frost sorting, and have thin silt-clay caps on upper surfaces. Moderate platy structure. Finely vesicular.

frost sorting affected the deposit prior to loess deposition. Sorted nets at the southern edge of the till-covered bench may have formed at the same time; the nets are large (5-7 m), and are presently inactive.

Archeological site 5 BL 152 is a campsite on the deposit (Fig. 21). Milling-slab fragments, a cobble handstone, and chipping debris from the site have no age connotations. However, the base of a Mount Albion Corner-notched projectile point (Fig. 20a) is estimated to date from between 5800 ± 125 BP (I-3267) and 5350 ± 130 BP (I-4419), based on the ages of excavated Mount Albion complex components elsewhere in the Indian Peaks (Benedict and Olson 1978). A projectile point/ knife of gray quartzite (Fig. 20b) is the same age or older; it has a weakly-defined stem, a shallowly-notched base, strongly-ground stem edges, collateral flaking, and serrated, alternately-beveled blade edges — all suggestive of late Paleo Indian or early Archaic affinities (see chapter 3).

EARLY SATANTA PEAK MORAINE (SPm1)

The outer of three end moraines in the study area (Fig. 7) crosses the valley at an altitude of 3410 m. The moraine is low and discontinuous. It consists of two main segments: a bouldery *terminal* ridge, along the axis of the valley; and a *left lateral* ridge,

atop low bedrock cliffs in the northwest corner of the map area. Intervening deposits have lost their morainal form due to slumping on the steep bedrock slope. Where slumping has occurred, the outer limit of early Satanta Peak till is marked by a residual concentration of very large Silver Plume granite erratics, buff to pink in color, with oriented microcline phenocrysts; the source of this rock type is an outcrop near the summit of Mount Neva (Fig. 4).

The terminal moraine has been trenched to a depth of 3-3½ m by the North Fork of Middle Boulder Creek. South of the stream, the moraine is treeless because of late-lying snow, and disappears beneath a lobe of the late Triple Lakes rock glacier complex (Fig. 23). North of the stream, flagged spruce and fir trees grow in dense tangles, shading an understory of blueberry (*Vaccinium myrtillus, V. scoparium*), Colorado currant (*Ribes coloradense*), subalpine daisy (*Erigeron perigrinus*), curled lousewort (*Pedicularis racemosa*), Jacob's ladder (*Polemonium delicatum*), and fireweed (*Chamerion angustifolium*). Tundra clearings support a patchwork of snow-accumulation communities, the dominant species of which vary with the length of the snow-free growing season.

The lateral moraine can be traced upvalley to an altitude of 3500 m, which is a first approximation of the steady-state equilibrium line altitude (ELA) of the North Fork glacier during early Satanta Peak time (Andrews 1975)[11]. Species such as *Kobresia myosuroides* indicate that this part of the moraine is neither ex-

Figure 23. View of the Fourth of July valley study area from cliffs overlooking the N. Fork of Middle Boulder Creek. An early Satanta Peak terminal moraine (SPm1) crosses the valley between two shallow ponds, disappearing beneath the front of a late Triple Lakes lobate rock glacier. Outwash terraces flanking the stream merge smoothly into the outer slope of a late Satanta Peak terminal moraine (SPm2). August 29, 1979.

[11] *Madole (1976b) estimates that the steady-state ELA during the Pinedale glacial maximum was 3170-3290 m.*

34

tremely windy nor buried beneath deep snow in winter (Bell and Bliss 1979). *R. geographicum* s.l. is better developed here than on other deposits in the valley (Fig. 19), reaching a maximum diameter of 154 mm. Other large lichens on the deposit include an *Acarospora chlorophana* thallus 234 mm in diameter, and an unidentified gray crustose lichen 530 mm in diameter. Depths of pitting and etching are comparable to those on the terminal moraine; lichens appear to be protecting the floors of many weathering pits from further granular disintegration. The damming effect of large boulders at the outer edge of the lateral moraine is responsible for steep distal slope angles at this locality (Fig. 9b).

Sixty quartz diorite cobbles were examined in slumped lateral deposits of early Satanta Peak age. Weathering-rind thicknesses ranged from 0 to 7 mm (Fig. 9f); the mean thickness (± 1σ) was 3.7 ± 1.2 mm (Fig. 9g). Because of the probability that two generations of cobbles are present (one exposed to near-surface chemical weathering since deposition of the moraine, and the other exposed for the first time by slumping), the *maximum* value is believed to be a better indicator of age than the *mean*. Unfortunately, no quartz diorite cobbles were found in undisturbed sectors of the early Satanta Peak moraine.

A soil profile in the terminal moraine south of the stream is shown in figure 24. An interesting feature of this profile is the concentration of iron oxide that occurs at the contact between the IIB2 horizon, which is loose and permeable, and the underlying IIICox horizon, which is compact and indurated. The latter is similar to the permafrost fragipans described by Van Vliet (1980). The B horizon has failed to reach maximum potential thickness at this locality because of the barrier to iron translocation represented by the IIICox horizon.

All of the artifacts in figure 20, except for those from site 5 BL 152, are from areas that were glaciated during the early Satanta Peak advance. Site 5 BL 162 is discussed in this section because it is in terrain that was never again covered with ice. The site is a multiple-component campsite on the south bank of the North Fork of Middle Boulder Creek (Fig. 13). It produced chipping debris, tool fragments, pieces of at least three sandstone milling slabs, and four projectile points. One of the latter (Fig. 20 *j*) is a Mount Albion Corner-notched point or related form. At least two others (Fig. 20 *h–i*), and possibly a third (Fig. 20 *g*, are of a style known locally as "Park" points (Stewart 1970); they are undated in the Southern Rockies, but appear to be related to the Gypsum point of the Great Basin and Colorado Plateau (Fowler *et al.* 1973, Jennings *et al.* 1980), a style that reached peak popularity between *ca.* 4000 and 3000 yr BP, and is known to have been used at high elevations (Simms 1979).

The Fourth of July Valley site (5 BL 120) is an excavated hunting camp on the moraine

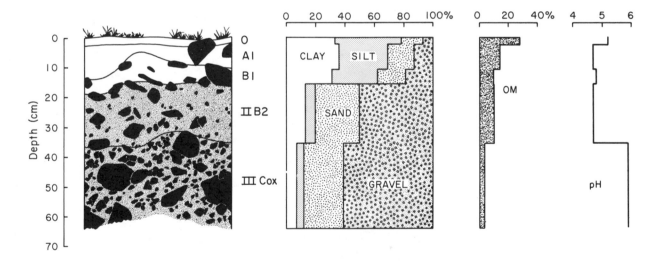

Comment: The profile was described beneath a tundra cover of *Silene acaulis, Minuartia obtusiloba, Acomastylis rossii, Salix arctica, Artemisia scopulorum, Selaginella densa, Carex rupestris*, grasses, and soil lichens. It consists of loess and reworked loess above glacial till.

O — Very dark brown (10YR 2/3 m) silty clay loam. Structureless. Abundant roots.

A1 — Dark brown (7.5YR 3/2 m) clay. Stones uncommon. Structureless. Scattered charcoal flecks have probably blown from site 5 BL 120.

B1 — Dark brown to brown (7.5YR 4/3 m) clay loam. Stones uncommon, but more numerous than in A1 horizon. Structureless. Lower boundary an erosion surface with stone concentration.

IIB2 — Dark brown (7.5YR 3/4 m) stony, gravelly sandy clay loam. Stones have frost-sorted coarse sand and fine gravel underlayers. Weak to moderate fine blocky structure. Lower boundary marked by 1-cm-thick 7.5YR 4/6 m oxidized layer.

IIICox — Grayish brown to light olive brown (2.5Y 5/3 m) stony, very gravelly sandy loam. Non-sorted. Stones have thin silt-clay caps, and are angular (33%), subangular (56%), subrounded (10%), and rounded (1%). Very compact; less permeable than underlying material.

Figure 24. Soil profile, early Satanta Peak terminal moraine, locality 2 (Fig. 13).

Figure 25. Outwash terraces and floodplain-bog deposits south of the early Satanta Peak lateral moraine (SPm1). The outwash was deposited during late Satanta Peak time, and was dissected soon after deglaciation. The photograph was taken from the Triple Lakes rock glacier shown in figure 23. October 1, 1979.

crest in the shadow of the rock glacier (Fig. 13). The site is discussed in chapter 3. In connection with the age of the moraine it suffices to say that the sequence of stratigraphic units and unconformities in the excavation area is so extraordinarily complex that it implies the passage of considerable time between deposition of the moraine and occupation. Dates for occupation are 5880 ± 120 BP (I-6544) and 6045 ± 120 BP (I-6545).

The position of the moraine in the valley shows that it is younger than deposits of the late stage of Pinedale Glaciation. Stratigraphic studies in the Fourth of July Valley Bog (p. 58) indicate that it is older than 9215 ± 105 radiocarbon years (I-11,092 avg.). I correlate it with the type Satanta Peak moraine at Caribou Lake (Benedict 1973a). Relative-dating criteria are consistent with this correlation, but cannot confirm it because of their inherent lack of resolution; rock types suitable for weathering-rind measurements are absent in the Caribou Lake valley.

Moraine orientations, striation directions, and boulder lithology suggest that the outer Satanta Peak moraine was deposited by a glacier that originated in snowfields south and east of the summit of Mount Neva, and along the north-facing wall of the valley. Compared to subsequent advances, its accumulation area was large. This was the final time that ice from the upper valley entered the study area.

SATANTA PEAK OUTWASH TERRACES (SPo) AND STRATH TERRACES (SPt)

Retreat of ice from the outer Satanta Peak terminal moraine created a basin in which proglacial lake silts, clays, and fine sands were deposited. These do not outcrop in the study area, but were encountered in excavations at site 5 BL 120 (Chapter 3) and in a ridge of disturbed lake and outwash sediments (TLsr) at the front of one of the rock-glacier lobes.

The lake survived only briefly before a readvance of Satanta Peak ice caused renewed coarse clastic sedimentation. Outwash deltas grew northward and eastward into the lake, filling its basin with cobbles, boulders, gravel, and sand to the level of a shallow spillway in the moraine crest. Part of the spillway is still visible north of the present outlet channel.

The outwash grades smoothly into the distal slope of a late Satanta Peak terminal moraine at the southern edge of the basin (Fig. 23), and is believed to have been derived partially from that source. However, its sediments include pebbles and cobbles of Silver Plume granite, which give eroded terrace remnants a pinkish color, and indicate a contribution from bedrock outcrops in the vicinity of Mount Neva. It is probable that a glacier existed independently in the upper valley at this time, and was an additional source of outwash.

Figure 26. Late Satanta Peak outwash terrace. Trees in the background mark the top of a scarp cut in early Satanta Peak till by the North Fork of Middle Boulder Creek as it meandered on its former floodplain. Vegetation differences are the result of moisture and snow-accumulation gradients. October 1, 1979.

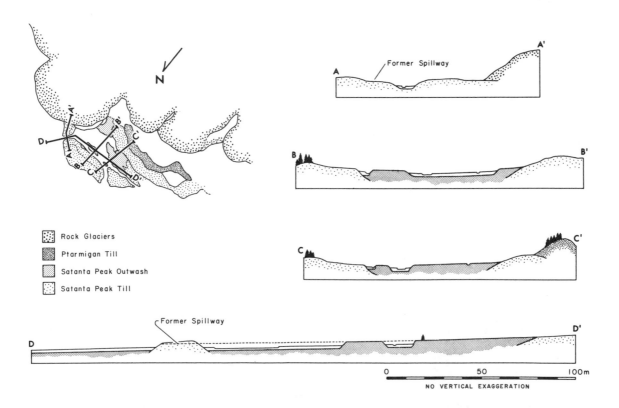

Rock Glaciers

Ptarmigan Till

Satanta Peak Outwash

Satanta Peak Till

Former Spillway

Former Spillway

0 50 100m

NO VERTICAL EXAGGERATION

Figure 27. Topographic profiles, Fourth of July valley study area.

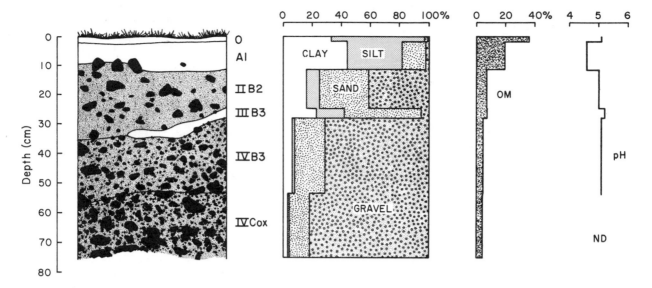

Comment: The profile was described beneath a dense tundra cover of *Vaccinium myrtillus*, *Acomastylis rossii*, *Silene acaulis*, *Minuartia obtusiloba*, *Sibbaldia procumbens*, *Deschampsia caespitosa*, and soil lichens. Sediments consist of outwash overlain by slightly reworked loess.

0	Very dark brown (10YR 2/2 m) silty clay loam. Stone-free and structureless. Roots abundant.
A1	Very dark brown (10YR 2/3 m) clay. Stones uncommon. Cohesive and structureless. Charcoal flecks in unit probably relate to archeological site 5 BL 154. Lower boundary an erosion surface.
IIB2	Dark yellowish brown (10YR 4/4-4/6 m) gravelly sandy clay loam. Chromas are strongest in upper part of unit. Cobbles are subangular, subrounded, and rounded, and rest on thin, frost-sorted sand and gravel layers. Weak fine blocky structure.

IIIB3	Dark yellowish brown (10YR 3/4-4/4 m) stone-free sandy clay loam. Moderate blocky structure. Discontinuous.
IVB3	Dark yellowish brown (10YR 3/4 m) cobbly, very gravelly sandy loam. Cobbles are subangular (27%), subrounded (61%), and rounded (12%), slightly imbricated, with fine gravel underlayers and thin (< 0.5 mm) silt-clay caps. Loose and structureless.
IVCox	Dark grayish brown to olive brown (2.5Y 4/3 m) cobbly, very gravelly sandy loam. Cobbles have well-developed gravel underlayers and weak silt-clay caps. Structureless.

Figure 28. Soil profile, late Satanta Peak outwash, locality 4.

After the basin had become filled with lake and outwash sediments, the North Fork of Middle Boulder Creek migrated back and forth for an undetermined length of time on its high floodplain, eroding laterally into adjacent till. An erosion surface and scarp were cut in the inner slope of the early Satanta Peak moraine north of the creek (Fig. 26); the base of the scarp slopes downvalley at an angle of 1½°-2°, indicating that it is not the strandline of a former proglacial lake. A buried erosion surface and scarp at site 5 BL 120 also developed at this time (Chapter 3), and ground moraine west of the main body of outwash was planed to the level of the high floodplain (Fig. 7).

Lateral planation was followed by an episode of downcutting, during which the former spillway was abandoned, the moraine was trenched, and the outwash plain behind it was dissected. Outwash and strath terraces were left standing 2-3 m above the present channel of the North Fork of Middle Boulder Creek (Figs. 25, 26). Relationships are illustrated by the topographic profiles in figure 27. Sediments that were flushed downstream when the moraine and high floodplain were dissected were deposited as levees on the floor of the present Fourth of July Valley Bog; ponds at the north and south edges of the bog (Fig. 7) owe their existence to these levees, which interrupted pre-existing drainage patterns.

Well-developed soils in till on the floor of the abandoned spillway (Fig. 9 i-1) and in terraces that flank the North Fork of Middle Boulder Creek (Fig. 28) suggest that relatively little time elapsed between deposition of the outwash and its dissection. Breaching of the moraine is likely to have resulted from a decrease in sediment supply, encouraging downcutting.

Each of the principal streams that cross the outwash surface responded differently to the change in base level. Because of its high discharge, the North Fork of Middle Boulder Creek eroded deeply into the terrace deposits, establishing a new, gentler gradient. The stream now flows in a relatively straight channel (sinuosity = 1.06)[12]. A tributary stream that enters the study area from the northwest was less able to erode; it crosses the strath terrace in a narrow, winding channel (sinuosity = 1.67), then downcuts deeply

[12] *Sinuosity is the ratio of channel length to valley length (Schumm 1977: 117).*

where it leaves the till and enters finer-textured outwash sediments. Meandering of the small stream on the strath terrace is interpreted as a channel-lengthening, energy-dissipating response to flow across a deposit with a steep, inherited gradient, and a boulder content that precluded significant downcutting.

The surfaces of the outwash terraces are light in color (Figs. 25, 26) due to eroded, stony plant communities in which the white soil lichen, *Lepraria arctica*, is an important component. Species such as blueberry (*Vaccinium myrtillus*), creeping wintergreen (*Gaultheria humifusa*), bog laurel (*Kalmia polifolia*), alpine avens (*Acomastylis rossii*), and sibbaldia (*Sibbaldia procumbens*) color the flanks of the terraces bright red in fall. Below the zone of vivid autumn coloration, trickles of meltwater seep from the terraces, causing small-scale slumping and solifluction. Water from the springs nourishes a mosaic of pond and bog communities (Fig. 25), in which marsh marigold (*Caltha leptosepala*), rose crown (*Clementsia rhodantha*), elephantella (*Pedicularis groenlandica*), rushes (*Juncus mertensianus*, *Eleocharis quinqueflora*), sedges (*Carex scopulorum*, *C. nigricans*, *C. illota*, *C. aquatilis*, *C. vernacula*), and mosses variously predominate. Along the banks of the North Fork of Middle Boulder Creek there is a splash-zone fringe of Parry primrose (*Primula parryi*) (Fig. 26).

Shallow differential weathering of outwash clasts (1.9-2.4 cm) is attributed to the scarcity of large boulders and the inefficiency with which mechanical-weathering processes attack stones with smooth, stream-polished surfaces. Depths of pitting are only about half as great as on the strath terrace to the north, where boulders were exposed to weathering at the same time, but were initially rougher-textured; boulders of biotite gneiss on the strath terrace are etched to a maximum depth of 5.1 cm, similar to the depth of etching on Satanta Peak terminal moraines in the study area (Fig. 9 e).

Seventeen quartz diorite cobbles were found in a stone-by-stone search of outwash terraces on both sides of the stream. The average weathering-rind thickness (4.5 ± 1.3 mm) and range of thicknesses (2½-7 mm) suggest that the outwash terraces are similar or identical in age to the late Satanta Peak moraine described in the following section (Fig. 9 f, g).

Several archeological sites occur on the terraces. Because it is unlikely that prehistoric hunters would have camped on the active floodplain of a glacial stream, or on the rocky surface of a terrace that had not yet acquired a cover of loess and vegetation, all of the sites are believed to post-date outwash dissection and loess deposition. The terraces were used intensively at least as early as the Middle Plains Archaic period, and probably earlier; widely scattered cultural remains reflect frequent visits.

Site 5 BL 169 straddles the contact between strath and outwash terraces north of the stream, a short distance upvalley from the former spillway (Fig. 13). It yielded chipping debris, a discoidal handstone of imported rhyolite porphyry, handstone and milling-slab fragments of Lyons sandstone, and a parallel-oblique-flaked cutting tool made of light gray quartzite; the site may represent an activity area of site 5 BL 120, across the stream, where similar quartzite was worked using an identical flaking technique about 5960 radiocarbon years ago (Chapter 3).

Site 5 BL 159, also north of the stream (Fig. 13), produced an end scraper, gray quartzite cutting tools, and fragments of a Lyons sandstone milling slab, but no diagnostic artifacts that could be used in estimating its age.

Site 5 BL 154, south of the stream (Fig. 13), produced flake knives, several large bifaces, Lyons sandstone milling-slab fragments, and chipping debris, scattered over a broad area. Included in flakes from the site were pieces of volcanic glass, uncommon in the Indian Peaks, and a diversity of other rock types from source areas east and west of the continental divide. A small, triangular biface (Fig. 20 c), possibly a projectile point, has no definite time connotations. The burinated stem of a gray quartzite projectile point with ground stem edges and ground, shallowly-indented base (Fig. 20 d) is estimated to be of Middle Plains Archaic age or older. Burination is a trait more-commonly associated with the Paleo-Indian and Early Archaic periods in the high mountains than with the Middle Plains Archaic period.

Indicative of the intensity with which outwash terraces in the study area were used by prehistoric man, two of three soil-profile pits dug in the deposits encountered charcoal from possible human campfires. One was at site 5 BL 154 (Fig. 13, locality 5). Here charcoal was found 16-19 cm below ground surface at the contact between very dark brown to dark brown loess, above, and brown, pebbly, reworked loess below (Fig. 29). There was no basal oxidation. However, fifteen outwash cobbles associated with the charcoal suggest that the feature was a stone-filled hearth; some of the stones were fractured and discolored by burning, and some were underlain by charcoal. No flakes, bone fragments, or artifacts were associated. A date of 3385 ± 95 BP (I-11,134) for charcoal from the hearth applies to one of several occupations of site 5 BL 154, and provides age control for the two-part loess sequence on this portion of the terrace. Pebbly reworked loess beneath the hearth becomes darker in color and richer in organic matter with depth (Fig. 29), suggesting that eroded soil humus was deposited with the loess during the early phases of its accumulation. Dates of 5910 ± 115 BP (I-11,370A, NaOH-insoluble) and 5420 ± 360 BP (I-11,370B, NaOH-soluble, HCl-insoluble) apply to formation of the eroded soil, and are consistent with other dates for *in situ* and redeposited late Altithermal humus horizons in the Indian Peaks (Benedict and Olson 1978, Benedict 1979c, Burns 1979).

A profile pit dug in an outwash terrace farther to the south (Fig. 13, locality 6) also

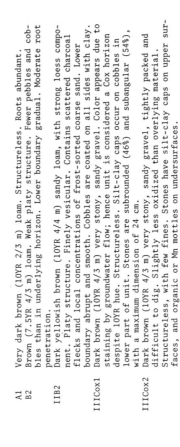

A1 — Very dark brown (10YR 2/3 m) loam. Structureless. Roots abundant.

B2 — Brown (7.5YR 4/3 m) loam. Weak platy structure. Fewer pebbles and cobbles than in underlying horizon. Lower boundary gradual. Moderate root penetration.

IIB2 — Dark yellowish brown (10YR 4/4 m) sandy loam, with strong loess component. Platy structure. Finely vesicular. Contains scattered charcoal flecks and local concentrations of frost-sorted coarse sand. Lower boundary abrupt and smooth. Cobbles are coated on all sides with clay.

IIICox1 — Dark brown (10YR 4/3 m) very stony, sandy gravel. Color appears due to staining by groundwater flow; hence unit is considered a Cox horizon despite 10YR hue. Structureless. Silt-clay caps occur on cobbles in lower part of unit. Stones are subrounded (46%) and subangular (54%), with a maximum dimension of 24 cm.

IIICox2 — Dark brown (10YR 4/3 m) very stony, sandy gravel, tightly packed and difficult to dig. Slightly less oxidized than overlying material. Structureless, with few fines. Stones have silt-clay caps on upper surfaces, and organic or Mn mottles on undersurfaces.

Figure 30. Soil profile, late Satanta Peak outwash, locality 6. Date is for charcoal. Absence of rounded boulders and Silver Plume granite erratics in the outwash suggests a local source, within the study area.

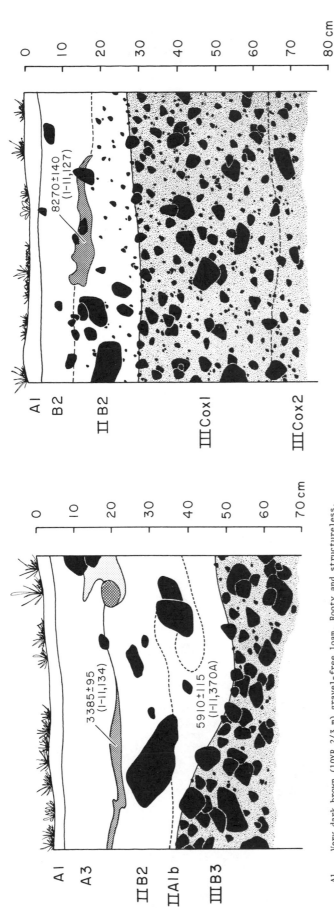

A1 — Very dark brown (10YR 2/3 m) gravel-free loam. Rooty and structureless.

A3 — Very dark brown to dark brown (10YR 2/3-3/3 m) gravel-free loam. Moderate fine platy structure. Stones in unit are oxidized and fractured by burning.

IIB2 — Brown (7.5YR 4/3 m) loam, sandier than A3 horizon. Pebbles and stones suggest reworking of loess by frost. Moderate fine platy structure; finely vesicular. Scattered charcoal flecks occur in upper part of deposit.

IIA1b — Dark brown (10YR 3/3 m) loam to sandy loam, texturally and structurally identical to IIB2 horizon, but richer in humus. Inverted sequence may indicate redeposition of an eroded soil, with A-horizon material first to accumulate on the terrace. Lower boundary an erosion surface.

IIIB3 — Dark yellowish brown (10YR 4/4 m) stony, gravelly loamy sand outwash, grading to 10YR 4/3 m at bottom of pit (90 cm). Stones are coated with clay, but lack Mn or organic stains. They are rounded (20%), subrounded (54%), and subangular (26%), with a maximum dimension of 26 cm.

Wood charcoal

Charcoal-filled krotovina

Strong brown (7.5YR 4/6 m) loamy sand, associated with krotovina

Figure 29. Soil profile, late Satanta Peak outwash, locality 5. Dates are for hearth charcoal and redeposited soil humus. Rounded cobbles and boulders are common in the outwash, suggesting an up-valley source.

encountered charcoal; here there was no surface indication of an archeological site. The
charcoal occurred as a small concentration at
12- to 17-cm depth (Fig. 30). It rested on
dark yellowish brown platy, vesicular reworked loess, and was overlain by brown loess,
also reworked. The contact between the two
loess units was distinct only where charcoal
was present. There were no flakes or artifacts, no burned stones, and no basal oxidation: i.e., no indication that the charcoal
was of cultural origin. A non-cultural origin,
however, would require a tree cover that does
not presently exist at this locality because
of late-lying snow. A date of 8270 ± 140 BP
(I-11,127) for the charcoal is a minimum age
for accumulation and reworking of the lower
loess unit.

All evidence considered, the early history of the study area appears to have been
approximately as follows: (1) the outer moraine was deposited during the first of two
Satanta Peak glacial advances; (2) lake sediments accumulated in a basin behind the moraine during ice recession; (3) outwash was
deposited during an advance to the inner Satanta Peak moraine; (4) the surface of the
outwash plain and adjacent till became graded
to the level of a shallow spillway in the
crest of the outer moraine; (5) the dam of
till was breached during early post-Satanta
Peak time; (6) the resulting change in base
level caused dissection of the outwash plain
and redeposition of pebble- and cobble-sized
material in the Fourth of July Valley Bog,

prior to 9215 ± 105 BP; and (7) a layer of
windblown silt accumulated atop the outwash
terraces prior to 8270 ± 140 yr BP, setting
the stage for intensive human occupation.

LATE SATANTA PEAK MORAINE (SPm2)

The middle of three terminal moraines in
the study area is a discrete ridge only at its
eastern end (Fig. 31), where it descends to
an altitude of 3420 m; farther to the west the
topographic form of the moraine is indistinct,
the till is thinner, and the deposit can no
longer be satisfactorily distinguished from
younger material (Fig. 7).

Striation directions indicate that the
moraine was deposited by ice that flowed in a
north-northeasterly direction, from snowfields
at the bases of north-facing cliffs. There is
no evidence of a connection to the glacier
that is believed to have existed independently
in the upper valley at this time.

The moraine is well vegetated and topographically subdued. Boulder frequency is low,
due in part to luxuriant plant growth and peat
development along streams and seeps. Irregular
large-scale sorted frost patterns occur in
seepage areas.

Spruce trees are uncommon on the moraine,
but are erect and tall compared to the fir
trees that form thickets on its distal slope;
the upper stems of many of the latter have
been killed in recent winters. Beneath the

Figure 31. Late Satanta Peak
terminal moraine (SPm2) and
outwash terraces. Trees near
the center of the photograph
are on outwash at archeological
site 5 BL 154. Late Triple
Lakes rock glaciers tower in
the background. July 16, 1979.

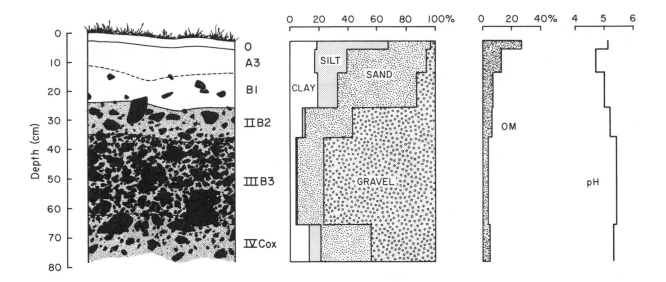

Comment: The profile was described beneath a tundra cover of *Vaccinium myrtillus, V. scoparium, Sibbaldia procumbens, Artemisia scopulorum, Acomastylis rossii, Salix arctica, Silene acaulis, Minuartia obtusiloba, Selaginella densa,* and *Carex* sp. Loess and reworked loess overlie till; openwork rubble in the IIIB3 horizon is believed to have formed by vertical frost sorting, and is the aquifer through which meltwater streams drain under the innermost moraine.

O   Very dark grayish brown (10YR 3/2 m) silt loam. Structure-less.

A3   Dark brown to brown (7.5YR 4/3 m) stone-free sandy loam. Moderate fine platy structure. Finely vesicular.

B1   Brown (7.5YR 5/3 m) sandy clay loam. Rare small pebbles. Moderate fine blocky structure. Finely vesicular.

IIB2   Dark yellowish brown (10YR 4/4-4/6 m) stony, very gravelly sandy loam. Weak fine blocky structure.

IIIB3   Dark yellowish brown (10YR 3/4 m) to olive brown (2.5Y 3/4 m) stony, very gravelly sandy loam. Local openwork areas. Loose and structureless.

IVCox   Olive gray (5Y 5/2 m) stony, gravelly sandy clay loam. Moderate to strong fine platy structure, with secondary blocky structure. Vesicular. Stones have thin silt-clay caps.

Figure 32. Soil profile, late Satanta Peak moraine, locality 7 (Fig. 13).

trees there is an understory of subalpine herbs and shrubs, similar to that on the outer Satanta Peak moraine. Well-drained clearings have a sparse cover of snow-tolerant mosses, soil lichens, and tundra herbs; springs that emerge at the contact between the late Satanta Peak and Ptarmigan moraines are flanked by lush meadows of sedge (*Carex scopulorum*), marsh marigold (*Caltha leptosepala*), tall mertensia (*Mertensia ciliata*), and Parry primrose (*Primula parryi*).

The range of weathering-rind thicknesses for 69 quartz diorite cobbles on the moraine was 3-7 mm; the mean thickness was 4.7 ± 1.1 mm. These measurements suggest that the moraine is similar in age to outwash terraces on the valley floor (Fig. 9 f, g).

The soil in the moraine crest is well developed (Fig. 32), with a generous thickness of loess and reworked loess (25 cm), a strongly-oxidized (7.5YR) and relatively thick (52 cm) B horizon, and a complex (5-unit) horizon sequence (Fig. 9). Till at the base of the profile is capped by a 25-cm-thick layer of loose stones and gravel, resulting from frost sorting or from winnowing of fines by flowing water. Because of the ridgetop location of the profile locality and its proximity to large-scale sorted patterned ground, frost sorting is considered to be the

most probable explanation.

No archeological sites have been identified on the deposit; however, sites 5 BL 166 and 5 BL 187 are in areas of striated bedrock that were glaciated during the late Satanta Peak advance (Fig. 13). Neither site closely controls the age of the moraine. From site 5 BL 187 there are a few undiagnostic chipped-stone tools, milling-slab fragments, and waste flakes, including a flake of clear volcanic glass. From site 5 BL 166 there are a large quartzite chopper, milling-slab fragments, bifaces, chipping debris, and two projectile points. The smaller point fragment (Fig. 20 e) is the base of a corner-notched arrowpoint, probably used within the past 1500 years. The larger point (Fig. 20 f) has an expanding stem and concave base, with heavy wear along its blade edges and tip; this point may date from either the Middle or Late Plains Archaic periods.

PTARMIGAN MORAINE (PTm)

The inner of three terminal moraines in the study area is a steep-fronted ridge of bouldery till perched piggyback upon the crest of the late Satanta Peak moraine, or nested

Figure 33. Fourth of July valley moraines and rock glaciers. The till ridge on the far shore of the pond (SPm1) marks the maximum downvalley extent of early Satanta Peak ice. In the far distance, a ridge of late Satanta Peak till (SPm2) protrudes from beneath a moraine of Ptarmigan age (PTm), its steep, bouldery front shaded from the late afternoon sun. Rock glaciers and talus cones complete the sequence. October 4, 1979.

against its inner slope (Fig. 33). The ridge consists of three connected arcs, the inner faces of which are approximately parallel to the lobate fronts of nearby rock glaciers (Fig. 7). Striation directions show that glacier flow was in a north-northeasterly or northerly direction. If lateral deposits were originally present at the western margin of the ice, they have long since been destroyed by erosion. The lowest altitude reached by the glacier that deposited the moraine was 3425 m.

Vegetation is similar to that on older moraine ridges, except that plant communities adapted to seepage areas and streamside marshes are absent. Drainage is entirely subsurface, through the deposit.

The damming effect of large boulders at the outer edge of the moraine contributes to its steep distal slope. Although the moraine is steeper-fronted and more bouldery than the deposit on which it rests, it is gentler and less bouldery than many sectors of the outer Satanta Peak moraine (Fig. 9 b, c). Maximum depths of pitting (2.3 cm) and etching (5.4 cm) are similar to those on other deposits, both older and younger, in the study area (Fig. 9 e).

Soil-profile development is comparable to that in moraines of Satanta Peak age (Fig. 34), except that soil horizons are fewer (3 above the Cox), and loess infiltration is shallower (12 cm). Better-developed soils, with redder hues, thicker loess mantles, and more-complicated horizon sequences, occur on

ground moraine of Ptarmigan age at site 5 BL 170 (Chapter 4).

Two trenches were dug in the distal slope of the moraine in search of *in situ* organic matter that could be radiocarbon dated. As practiced in southern Norway by Griffey and Matthews (1978) this is an elegant technique that has provided close maximum ages for glacial deposits (however, see Matthews 1980). As practiced in the Fourth of July valley by ourselves, it was a Sisyphean exercise in moving large boulders for little purpose. No buried vegetation or soil humus were found in either profile. At one locality the moraine rested directly upon bedrock. At the other it rested upon till of late Satanta Peak age, the surface of which consisted of cobbles and boulders without a matrix of fines. The rubble layer, which was 30-35 cm thick and resembled the IIIB3 horizon in figure 32, may have resulted from upfreezing of stones or from winnowing of fines by water prior to burial; soil humus (if originally present) did not survive the process.

A minimum age for the moraine was obtained at the Ptarmigan site (5 BL 170), an excavated campsite on till of this advance (Chapter 4). The till was overlain by glaciofluvial gravels, colluvium, and two loess units, the lower of which had been redeposited by slopewash processes. The oldest of several hearths at the site was a charcoal-filled basin that originated at the surface of the colluvium. Dates for replicate charcoal samples are 6450 ± 110 BP (I-7458) and 6205 ± 170 BP (I-10,976); a

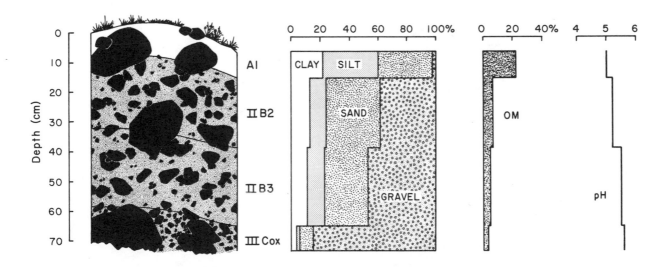

Comment: The profile was described beneath a tundra cover of *Vaccinium myrtillus, Artemisia scopulorum, Erigeron simplex, Acomastylis rossii, Silene acaulis, Carex phaeocephala, C. pelocarpa*, and grasses. Sediments are till and frost-disturbed till with a surface mantle of loess.

A1 Very dark grayish brown (10YR 3/2 m) loam, grading downward to dark brown (10YR 3/3-4/3 m). Weak blocky structure. Firm, due to densely-matted rootlets.
IIB2 Dark yellowish brown (10YR 4/4 m) stony, gravelly sandy clay loam. Slightly redder than underlying horizon. Moderate fine blocky structure.

IIB3 Dark yellowish brown (10YR 4/4 m) to olive brown (2.5Y 4/4 m) stony, gravelly sandy loam to sandy clay loam. Moderate fine blocky structure.
IIICox Dark grayish brown to olive brown (2.5Y 4/3 m) stony, very gravelly sandy clay loam. Loose and structureless.

Figure 34. Soil profile, Ptarmigan moraine, locality 8 (Fig. 13).

44

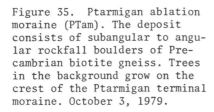

Figure 35. Ptarmigan ablation moraine (PTam). The deposit consists of subangular to angular rockfall boulders of Precambrian biotite gneiss. Trees in the background grow on the crest of the Ptarmigan terminal moraine. October 3, 1979.

Figure 36. Lodgement till (PTgm) and striated bedrock exposed when overlying glacial ice and ablation till moved eastward (to the right), accumulating in flow lobes at the base of the steep slope. The striations shown in figure 8 were photographed on these two outcrops. September 10, 1979.

weighted average date of 6380 ± 95 BP, calculated using the method of Long and Rippeteau (1974), is taken as a minimum age for deposition of the moraine.

Weathering-rind data suggest that the deposit is closer in age to the Ptarmigan site than to Satanta Peak moraines downvalley. Rind thicknesses ranged from 2 to 4 mm in eight quartz diorite cobbles, averaging 3.1 ± 0.8 mm (Fig. 9 f, g). Assuming that the inner Satanta Peak moraine (average rind thickness 4.7 ± 1.1 mm) is 10,000-11,000 radiocarbon years old and that rind formation is a linear function of time, an age of *ca.* 6600-7250 radiocarbon years is suggested. If rind thickness is a logarithmic function of time (Colman 1977), an age near the younger end of the suggested time span (but not less than 6380 years) is most probable.

The name "Ptarmigan" is proposed, informally, for Front Range ice advances that are older than an interval of warmth and soil formation that began in the Indian Peaks *ca.* 6000 radiocarbon years ago, but are younger by several millenia than the youngest Satanta Peak advances.

PTARMIGAN ABLATION MORAINE (PTam)

East of site 5 BL 170, ground moraine of Ptarmigan age is buried beneath angular to subangular boulders of biotite gneiss (Fig. 35), believed to be of rockfall origin. A single rockfall event is suggested, although not proven, by the sharply-defined western boundary of the deposit (Fig. 7). Because angular debris extends to the crest of the Ptarmigan terminal moraine, but nowhere overlaps onto its distal slope, it seems most probable that the rockfall came to rest on ice, and was transported to the moraine by glacial flow. I have mapped it as ablation moraine of the Ptarmigan advance.

The surface of the deposit slopes to the east, parallel to the crest of the terminal moraine. One sector is particularly steep; here the ablation till has stretched and parted, forming a "window" through which striated bedrock and lodgement till can be seen (Fig. 36). Boulders in the lodgement till are subangular to subrounded, and include a diversity of rock types comparable to those in the terminal moraine.

Opening of the steeply-sloping "till window" produced massive lobate accumulations of angular ablation till at its base (Fig. 7). These features are flow lobes that formed by gravity movement during the final stages of ice wastage, when glacier surface gradients were no longer sufficient to sustain north-northeasterly flow. Movement involved ablation till and surviving remnants of the underlying glacier, but did not affect lodgement till beneath the ice.

If the ice had been thicker or the ablation till had provided better insulation, the deposit might have evolved into a lobate rock glacier.

PTARMIGAN OR EARLY TRIPLE LAKES ROCK GLACIER (rg)

South of the Ptarmigan site, a lobe of vegetated debris bridges the re-entrant between two active rock glaciers. Little can be said about the deposit, due to the small area exposed, except that it is older than the rock glaciers that have overridden it, and that the steepness of its front (Fig. 9 b) is such that it could be either an inactive rock glacier or a moraine.

In mapping the deposit as a rock glacier (Fig. 7) I am influenced by previous work in the Caribou Lake and Diamond Lake valleys (Fig. 2), where two generations of lobate rock glaciers alternate with one another along the bases of north-facing cliffs. The older lobes, like this deposit, are blanketed with fines, and are well-vegetated and topographically subdued; the younger lobes consist largely of openwork rubble, are sparsely vegetated, and topographically fresh.

The age of the deposit is uncertain. It could have formed during recession from the Ptarmigan terminal moraine, or during a more-recent ice advance. Rock-weathering characteristics do not clearly distinguish it from younger or older deposits in the study area (Fig. 9 d, e); quartz diorite cobbles are absent, precluding weathering-rind measurements. The soil on the rock glacier (Fig. 37) is relatively well developed, despite the unknown length of time required for fines to accumulate. There is no evidence for ongoing movement that would suggest surviving ice within the deposit.

LATE TRIPLE LAKES ROCK GLACIERS (TLrg)

The most extensive map unit in the study area is the rubble apron at the base of steep cliffs along the south edge of the valley (Fig. 7). Included in the unit are undifferentiated talus deposits of complex origin and age, and a series of strikingly-developed lobate rock glaciers (Wahrhaftig and Cox 1959), the largest of which is about 200 m wide and extends 200-250 m from the valley wall (Fig. 23). Differences in etching of gneissic boulders (Fig. 9 e) hint at the possibility that several generations of lobes are represented; however, movement has blurred contact relationships that may have formerly existed, and the effects of a persistent snowcover preclude the use of lichenometry for age separation. There are no rock types suitable for weathering-rind studies. I have mapped the deposits as a single unit, although others may wish to subdivide them further.

The fronts of the rock glaciers terminate at altitudes of 3420-3460 m, and slope at angles of 31°-44°. Steepness and sorting vary along the fronts of individual lobes, suggesting that certain sectors are moving more rapidly than others. An example of an active lobe front is shown in figure 38. It is considered active because its slope of 42°-44° exceeds the

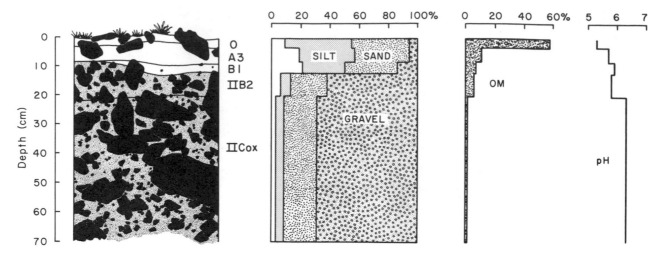

Comment: The profile was described beneath a tundra cover of *Sibbaldia procumbens*, *Selaginella densa*, *Carex* sp., and *Lepraria arctica*. The sequence of deposits consists of reworked loess above rock-glacier or debris-flow rubble. Fines may not have accumulated until long after the rock glacier became stabilized.

O   Very dark brown (10YR 2/3 m) loam. Stones and lag gravel at surface of unit are the result of frost heaving, rockfall, or avalanching. Structureless.

A3   Dark brown (10YR 3/3 m) loam. Contains fewer stones than O horizon. Structureless and finely vesicular.

B1   Dark yellowish brown (10YR 4/4 m) loam, similar to A3 horizon except in color. Discontinuous. Lower boundary an erosion surface.

IIB2 Yellowish brown (10YR 5/4 m) stony gravelly sandy loam. Undersurfaces of stones are mottled reddish purple by manganese or organic pigments. Structureless.

IICox Grayish brown to light olive brown (2.5Y 5/3 m) stony, gravelly sandy loam. Stones are subangular (64%) and angular (36%). Loose and structureless, with local areas of openwork rubble.

Figure 37.   Soil profile, Ptarmigan or early Triple Lakes rock glacier, locality 9 (Fig. 13).

Figure 38.   Unstable front of an active late Triple Lakes lobate rock glacier, southeast of the Ptarmigan site. July 27, 1979.

angle of repose for talus; its surface layer of large, lichen-covered boulders forms a relatively sharp angle with its front; its front is fine textured, sparsely vegetated, free of lichens, and unstable; and talus at the base of the front includes boulders with lichen-covered undersurfaces and powdery impact scars. The fronts of inactive rock glaciers slope more gently and can be climbed without releasing cascades of rock and gravel; their upper surfaces and fronts intersect in smooth arcs; their fronts are vegetated or banked with lichen-covered boulders; their talus aprons are commonly overgrown by bog or alpine turf vegetation

The surfaces of the rock glaciers consist of large angular to subangular boulders, generally without interstitial fine material. Troughs filled with late-lying or perennial snow separate some of the features from active talus cones along the south valley wall; where snowbanks are absent, the transition from rock glacier to talus is gradational. The surfaces of the rock glaciers show no conical pits, meandering furrows, or other thermokarst features (Wahrhaftig and Cox 1959), and no arcuate transverse ridges. The lithology of each lobe closely mirrors the composition of the bedrock cliff from which it is derived; biotite gneiss is the most common rock type on all lobes, with granite additionally present near the middle of the sequence, beneath an outcrop of that rock type.

Differences in lichen cover on the surfaces of the rock glaciers reflect differences in the persistence of snow. Lichen cover is densest, and *R. geographicum* s.l. thalli largest, on the north (moist) sides of large boulders in winter snow-free areas near the fronts of the treads. Species such as *Lecanora thomsonii* and *Lecidea atrobrunnea*, which are less tolerant than *R. geographicum* of competition, reach maximum diameters in lichen-kill zones of Audubon age near the rear of the debris apron, where total lichen cover is sparse.

Vascular plant cover varies with snow accumulation, stability of substrate, and the presence or absence of fine debris. Areas that consist only of openwork rubble lack vascular plants. Best vegetated is the rock-glacier lobe directly south of site 5 BL 120 (Fig. 23), where fine material has accumulated due to debris flows, avalanching, and wind. Prostrate and flagged subalpine fir trees grow near the axis of the lobe; *Dryas octopetala*, *Kobresia myosuroides*, and *Carex rupestris* grow in a snow-free zone behind its front. The front itself, above the level of late-lying snow, has an unusually rich vascular flora, which includes such showy blooming species as spotted saxifrage (*Saxifraga bronchialis*), whiplash saxifrage (*S. flagellaris*), the rare-and-endangered alpine poppy (*Papaver kluanense*), old-man-of-the-mountain (*Hymenoxys grandiflora*), Colorado blue columbine (*Aquilegia caerulea*), alpine primrose (*Primula angustifolia*), moss campion (*Silene acaulis*), and death camas (*Zigadenus elegans*), in addition to such common rock-glacier species as

alpine sorrel (*Oxyria digyna*), sky pilot (*Polemonium viscosum*), western yellow paintbrush (*Castilleja occidentalis*), green mertensia (*Mertensia viridis*), thistle (*Cirsium scopulorum*), and ragwort (*Senecio fremontii, S. eremophilus*).

The surfaces of two of the lobes have step-like longitudinal profiles. There is no evidence that the steps reflect multiple advances, velocity differences, or reactivation of headward areas. More probably they indicate subsurface topography in the form of buried bedrock ledges, ice faces, or older deposits.

I found no opportunity to examine the interiors of rock glaciers in the study area. However, steep, active fronts indicate surviving internal ice. The absence of thermokarst features such as conical pits and meandering furrows may indicate that the ice is interstitial (i.e., that the rock glaciers are ice-cemented rather than ice-cored), or that an ice core exists, but is covered with a layer of debris so thick that such features cannot form. Observations in mine tunnels and open-pit caving operations at localities in the San Juan Mountains (Brown 1925) and Tenmile Range (author's unpublished data) show that cores of snowbank or glacier ice are common in such deposits. The possibility that rock glaciers in the Fourth of July valley study area contain buried glaciers or snowbanks should not be discounted.

Regardless of the nature of the internal ice, the layer of coarse debris that forms the sole of the rock-glacier apron near its front contains ice-free channels that allow meltwater streams to flow within the rubble (Fig. 7).

Rates of rock-glacier movement have been measured at several localities in the Colorado Rocky Mountains (Outcalt and Benedict 1965, Bryant 1971, White 1971, C. Miller 1973, Stanton 1979). Particularly relevant to the Fourth of July valley is a study carried out near Green Lake No. 5, at an altitude of 3620 m in the Boulder City Watershed. Here measurements begun by Wallace (1967) and continued by White (1976b) established that boulders in the active (35°-42°) front and sides of a partially-vegetated lobate rock glacier were moving outward from the north-facing valley wall at an average rate of 1.4 cm/yr. This is a reasonable estimate for similar rock glaciers in the Fourth of July valley study area, remembering that certain sectors of their fronts are likely to move more rapidly, and that others may remain motionless for long periods of time.

Maximum *R. geographicum* s.l. diameters of 90 to 116 mm (Fig. 19) suggest ages of 2600 to 3500 years for the lichen communities that grow on individual rock-glacier lobes. If the lichens are original colonists, their diameters provide age estimates for the deposits. Alternately, they may date the end of an episode of expanded snowcover that was similar to, but more extensive than, that of Audubon time; or may record the time required for surface boulders to travel to the front of the rock glacier from the leading edges of lichen-kill zones at the rear of the debris apron; or may date stabilization of the rubble layer after a period of rapid advance. Without additional evidence there is no way to evaluate the significance of the lichenometric dates, other than to treat them as minimum ages.

Rock glaciers in this map unit (TLrg) are stratigraphically younger than the rock-glacier lobe (rg) described in the preceding section. Evidence that the age difference may be substantial includes steep frontal slope angles, which indicate the survival of internal ice, and a weakly-developed soil profile. The profile (Fig. 39) shows no evidence of B-horizon oxidation, suggesting that significantly less time was available for soil formation here than in the older rock-glacier lobe. However, as mentioned previously, front angles and soil development are unreliable age criteria when dealing with rock glaciers.

Previous attempts to date lobate rock glaciers in Front Range alpine valleys have been unsuccessful. In the Fourth of July valley study area, however, there is evidence that the largest lobe of the late Triple Lakes rock-glacier apron (Fig. 23) advanced rapidly to within a few meters of its modern position between 3300 and 3000 radiocarbon years ago.

(1) At archeological site 5 BL 120 (Chapter 3), angular boulders from the rock-glacier front are scattered across the excavation area, and occur in loess and fine-textured outwash sediments *above* the occupation surface. No such boulders occur in stratigraphic units *below* the occupation surface, suggesting that the rock glacier had not yet arrived at the southern margin of the site 5960 ± 85 radiocarbon years ago (average of I-6544, I-6545), when the site was occupied.

(2) At the "sand-ridge" locality discussed on pp. 49-53, advance of the rock glacier across soft lake and outwash sediments caused deformation and burial of a former land surface and soil. Archeological evidence indicates that the land surface was visited by people of the Mount Albion complex prior to its burial. Radiocarbon dates for the Mount Albion complex elsewhere in the region (5800-5350 BP) suggest a maximum age for arrival of the rock glacier, formation of the sand ridge, and burial of the former land surface.

(3) A concentration of spruce cones, needles, and twigs deep within the Fourth of July Valley Bog (pp. 59-60) suggests that cone-bearing spruce trees grew directly upwind from the sampling locality as recently as 4220 ± 70 radiocarbon years ago (I-11,652 avg.). Trees are currently excluded from this area by a late-lying snowbank that exists because of heavy winter accumulation of windblown snow in a pocket of calm air at the rock-glacier front. The rock glacier must have been absent 4220 radiocarbon years ago in order for trees to grow at the site.

(4) Also in the Fourth of July Valley Bog, a 15- to 23-cm-thick layer of micaceous silt and sand, believed to have washed from the front of the rock glacier as it advanced to its approximate modern position, rests upon peat with an age of 3340 ± 65 radiocarbon years (I-11,091 avg.), and is overlain by peaty muck with an age of 2970 ± 65 radiocarbon years (I-11,090 avg.). These dates closely bracket arrival of the rock glacier.

(5) The largest *R. geographicum* s.l. thallus growing on the surface of the rock glacier has a diameter of 110 mm (Fig. 19), and an estimated age of 3275 radiocarbon years. It is part of a lichen community that became established on the rock glacier following the period of rapid advance.

Based on the radiocarbon and lichenometric evidence outlined above, I conclude that the largest lobe of the late Triple Lakes rock gla-

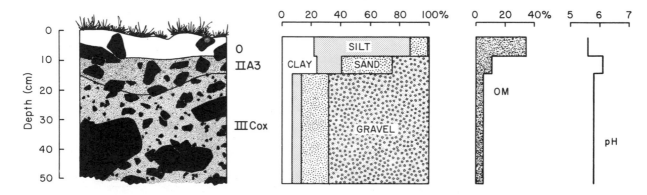

Comment: The profile was described beneath a tundra cover of *Acomastylis rossii*, *Salix arctica*, *Zigadenus elegans*, *Dryas octopetala*, *Silene acaulis*, *Carex rupestris*, and mosses. It is developed in mudflow debris with a surface layer of loess.

O   Very dark brown (10YR 2/3 m) silt loam. Loose and structureless. Lower boundary abrupt and smooth.

IIA3   Dark brown (10YR 3/3 m) stony sandy clay loam. Stones are angular to subangular, with weak Mn or organic stains on undersurfaces. Structureless. Lower boundary gradual and wavy.

IIICox   Dark grayish brown to olive brown (2.5Y 4/3 m) stony sandy clay loam. Stones are angular (24%), subangular (71%), and subrounded (5%); lower surfaces are stained reddish-purple by Mn oxides or organic pigments. Gravel underlayers are prominent; silt-clay caps are absent. Loose and structureless.

Figure 39. Soil profile, late Triple Lakes rock glacier, locality 10 (Fig. 13).

cier apron advanced rapidly, for an appreciable distance, between about 3300 and 3000 radiocarbon years BP. If the rock glacier originated by slow accumulation of talus and
accretion of interstitial ice (Wahrhaftig and
Cox 1959, Barsch 1977), its formation may have
preceded the interval of rapid advance by centuries or millenia. If, however, the rock glacier developed catastrophically, by rockfall
onto the surface of a glacier or perennial
snowbank (Benedict 1973b, Whalley 1974, Griffey and Whalley 1979), and subsequently moved
only a short distance, the time of formation
and time of arrival at its modern location may
have been essentially identical.

SAND RIDGE (TLsr)

Introduction. Southwest of site 5 BL 120, the
largest lobe of the late Triple Lakes rock
glacier has advanced across soft, easily-
deformable lake and bog sediments. Here, for a
distance of about 80 m, its front is parallel-
ed by a ridge of intricately-folded and brecciated gravel, sand, and silt. For want of a
better name, I refer to the feature as a "sand
ridge". No comparable ridge occurs where the
rock glacier terminates on till or bedrock.

Similar features have not previously been
reported in the literature, although a photograph taken by Breckenridge (1974, Fig. 2) in
the Absaroka Mountains, Wyoming, suggests that
they may occur elsewhere.

The ridge consists of two distinct arcuate segments (Fig. 7). The southernmost seg-
ment is formed by a half-dozen small, coalescing earth lobes, aligned along the shore of
an ephemeral meltwater pond. Each lobe is concentric around a large boulder, and is composed of micaceous pond-floor silts and sands
with an admixture of cobbles derived from the
outwash terrace that underlies the pond. Relationships between this ridge and a much-larger
feature to the north are unclear. The two deposits do not necessarily have the same origin
or age; the smaller ridge appears to be an impact feature formed by rockfall from the rock-
glacier front into soft pond sediments.

Detailed studies were restricted to the
larger ridge, which is better defined and
stratigraphically more complex. It rises above
the modern floodplain in a boggy area produced
by dissection of the late Satanta Peak outwash
plain (Figs. 7, 40). The ridge is 10 to 12 m
wide and 2.1 to 2.7 m high. Its distal slope
(16°-27°) is comparable to the distal slopes
of nearby end moraines (Fig. 9 b). Where erosion has removed turf from the surface of the
ridge, it has exposed lake silts and sands of
neutral hue, and brightly oxidized outwash
sands and gravels. Nonsorted circles (Washburn
1980) with terraced centers and bulging, vegetated frontal banks occur where silty sediments predominate.

The ridge is separated from the rock glacier by a trough 1.0 to 1.5 m deep (Fig. 41).
The trough is floored with angular to subangu-

lar gneissic and granitic boulders that have
fallen from the surface of the rock glacier;
boulders locally fill the trough and spill
across the crest and distal slope of the
ridge, forming a fringe of rock along its outer margin (Fig. 40).

Internal Structure. The ridge was trenched at
several localities (Fig. 13). Figure 42 illustrates the folded, brecciated nature of the
sediments at locality 11. Poorly-sorted cobble-
gravel outwash near the base of the profile
dips eastward and southeastward, in the direction of the rock glacier, at angles as steep
as 45°; the deposit is similar to Satanta Peak
outwash at site 5 BL 120 (units A-1, B-3, C-3,
D-2) and at profile locality 6 (Fig. 30).
Finer-textured outwash units in the profile
(Fig. 42) are better sorted, and resemble outwash from the rock glacier, as seen in the excavation area at site 5 BL 120 (units C-7,
D-3). Lake silts and fine sands in the profile
are believed to have accumulated in the proglacial lake that existed here during mid-
Satanta Peak time.

Similar sediments were encountered at profile locality 12, although only lake silts and
fine-textured outwash sands and gravels from
the rock glacier can be seen in figure 43. Beginning about 85 cm beneath the crest of the
ridge, and hidden from view in figure 43 by
the front wall of the profile pit, a tilted
block of cobble-gravel outwash dipped to the
southeast, toward the rock glacier, at an angle
of 65°. A 7-cm-thick A1 horizon was developed
in the upper part of the outwash block. The A1
horizon did not contain sufficient organic matter for radiocarbon dating (J. Buckley, pers.
comm. 1980); however, archeological evidence
suggests a probable Altithermal age.

Archeology. The projectile point illustrated
in figure 44 was found in a sample of humus-
rich cobble-gravel outwash collected from the
floor of the profile pit at locality 12 for radiocarbon dating and pebble-roundness measurements. The point was not found in situ. However, slumping from the pit wall can be excluded, because the floor of the pit was cleaned
in preparation for sampling. The sharp, unworn
blade edges and light buff color of the point
distinguish it from pebbles in the outwash,
which are rounded to subangular and stained
reddish-purple on all surfaces. By process of
elimination, the projectile point is likely to
have originated in the buried A1 horizon. I
conclude that the outwash surface was visited
by man during a period of soil development
that preceded formation of the sand ridge.

The point is stylistically different from
points found at the Fourth of July Valley site,
a few tens of meters to the northeast (Chapter
3), and is made of quartzite from a different
source (cf. Dakota Formation). Its closest
typological relationships lie with stemmed
points and knives of the Mount Albion complex
(Benedict and Olson 1978, Fig. 38 v-x, Fig.
55 r). As such, it is likely to be 5800 to
5350 radiocarbon years old, and the soil with

Figure 40. View of the "sand ridge" (TLsr) from the top of the largest late Triple Lakes rock glacier in the study area. The ridge is composed of folded and brecciated lake silts and outwash sediments, and is believed to be a push moraine or loading phenomenon. The topographic profile in figure 41 crosses the trough between sand ridge and rock glacier at the approximate location of the photographer's shadow. September 18, 1979.

which it was associated is likely to have been exposed at the ground surface during the late Altithermal.

Origin. Several hypotheses of sand-ridge origin were considered. The possibility that the ridge is a protalus rampart was rejected because of its composition and internal structure, and because similar ridges do not occur at the fronts of rock glaciers that terminate on till or bedrock. More probably the ridge is a push moraine or loading phenomenon. Variations of one or both of these hypotheses have been suggested as explanations for small moraine ridges formed subaqueously, or in association with ice-marginal lakes or meltwater-

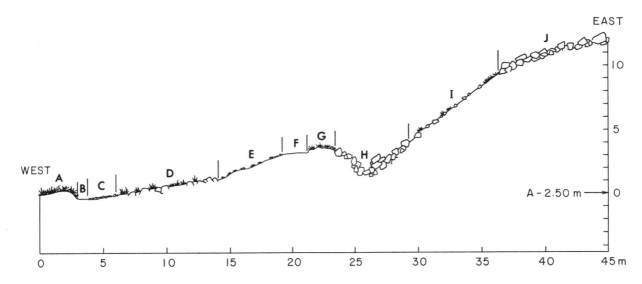

Figure 41. Topographic profile and vegetation transect across the sand ridge and rock-glacier front. No vertical exaggeration. The altitude of benchmark A, at profile locality 2 (Fig. 13), is taken as 0.0 m. _A_, *Carex scopulorum-Carex illota-Caltha leptosepala* bog; _B_, meltwater stream; _C_, bare cobbles; _D_, boulder apron with *Deschampsia caespitosa* meadow; _E_, eroded *Sibbaldia procumbens-Artemisia scopulorum-Acomastylis rossii-Salix arctica-Lepraria arctica* late-snowbed community; _F_, bare gravel at base of erosion scarp; _G_, eroded, frost-disturbed community of *Carex* sp., *Lepraria arctica*, *Silene acaulis*; _H_, openwork boulders; _I_, moderately stable rock-glacier front, with *Oxyria digyna*, *Silene acaulis*, *Cirsium scopulorum*, *Carex rupestris*; _J_, openwork boulders with mature lichen cover.

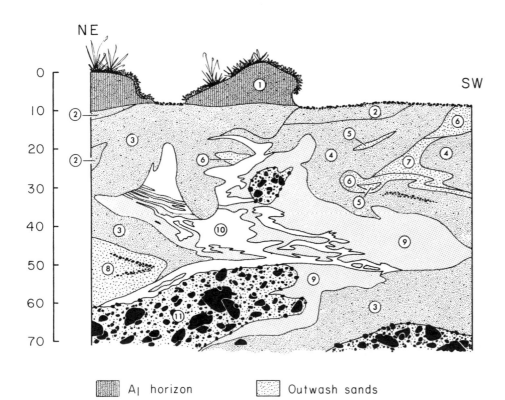

Figure 42. Section parallel to crest of sand ridge, profile locality 11 (Fig. 13). Lake deposits are fine textured and well sorted; outwash is coarser textured and moderately to poorly sorted. Moist colors for numbered units are:

(1) 2.5Y 4/4	(7) 5Y 5/3
(2) 5Y 5/2	(8) 7.5YR 5/6
(3) 2.5Y 5/4	(9) 2.5Y 5/4
(4) 10YR 5/4	(10) 2.5Y 5/3
(5) 5Y 5/1	(11) 2.5Y-
(6) 5YR 4/8	10YR 5/4

Legend:
- A₁ horizon
- Lake silts
- Lake sands
- Outwash sands
- Outwash sands & gravels
- Outwash gravels & cobbles

52

Figure 43. Folded and brecciated lake and outwash sediments in a profile parallel to
the crest of the sand ridge at
locality 12. Deposits visible
above the near wall of the
trench resemble the finer facies at locality 11. Hidden
from view is a detached, tilted block of cobble-gravel outwash. Developed in the upper 7
cm of the outwash is a weakly-
organic A1 horizon, 10YR 4/3 m
in color.

saturated till, at the fronts of glaciers in
the Canadian Arctic (Andrews and Smithson
1966), Iceland (Price 1969, 1970), and Norway
(Worsley 1974).

Push-Moraine Hypothesis. Push-moraine ridges
in the Netherlands and Germany are composed
of sand, gravel, and clay with a thin veneer
of till. Sedimentary layers strike parallel
to the axes of the ridges, and dip up-glacier
at angles of 25° to 70° (DeJong 1952, Rutten
1960). Folds and thrust faults are common
(Embleton and King 1975).

According to one variation of the push-
moraine hypothesis, the sand ridge was created by the bulldozing action of a glacier
that advanced across outwash and lake sediments during Ptarmigan or early Triple Lakes
time, prior to formation of the rock glacier.
An objection to this version of the hypothesis is the absence of a till mantle: boulders
associated with the sand ridge (Fig. 40) are
identical in lithology and rounding to boulders on the rock-glacier surface, and are believed to have fallen from that source. Another objection is the close parallelism that
exists between the ridge and the rock-glacier
front: if the sand ridge and the rock glacier
developed at different times and by different
processes, it seems an unlikely coincidence
that they should now be so closely spaced and
so precisely parallel.

According to a second variation of the
push-moraine hypothesis, the ridge was bull-
dozed into place by the advancing rock gla-

cier. Because the deposits are separated by a
broad trough, the ridge could only have formed
if the "push" were exerted through snow or ice
banked against the rock-glacier front. This is
not seen as a serious objection to the hypothesis.

Loading Hypothesis. According to the loading
hypothesis, the ridge developed because water-
saturated lake sediments and fine-textured outwash were unable to support the weight of the
advancing rock glacier, which settled into the
soft material, displacing it laterally, and ex-
truding it as a ridge beyond the rock-glacier
front. The loading hypothesis is consistent
with the location, composition, and internal
structure of the sand ridge.

Age. The sand ridge is younger than 5800-5350
radiocarbon years, the estimated age of the
projectile point buried beneath it. It is older than 1600 years, the age of a 62-mm *R. geographicum* s.l. thallus growing on its surface[13].
All factors considered, including the two most
probable origins of the feature (loading and
rock-glacier push), a late Triple Lakes age
appears to be most likely.

Survival of the sand ridge for at least
1600 years, and probably for twice that length
of time, suggests that during this period the

---

[13] *Because the ridge is in an area affected by
Audubon snowbank expansion, the lichen date
is not necessarily a close minimum.*

rock glacier was inactive, or was moving much more slowly than the average rate of 1.4 cm per year reported by White (1976*b*) from the Green Lakes valley. Otherwise the ridge would have been overridden long ago. Slow movement is consistent with the rich and varied flora of the rock-glacier front (p. 47), and with the fact that only minor quantities of sand and silt have washed from the feature into the Fourth of July Valley Bog since the initial influx of clastic sediments about 3300-3000 ^{14}C yr ago.

A second possible reason that the deposit has not been buried by the rock glacier is that the two features are moving in tandem, with the sand ridge advancing like the forebulge of an ice sheet or the bow wave of a ship. A movement study would establish whether or not such a process is operating.

THE FOURTH OF JULY VALLEY BOG

Introduction. The Fourth of July Valley Bog occupies an irregularly-shaped bedrock basin downstream from the outer Satanta Peak terminal moraine (Fig. 7). A late Triple Lakes lobate rock glacier stands 5-10 m to the south, on Pinedale ground moraine. Water from the rock glacier and surrounding slopes enters the bog via small streams and seeps, and exits through the incised narrow channel of the North Fork of Middle Boulder Creek. The stream channel is walled with peat and muck, and floored with bouldery outwash.

I cored the bog at close-spaced intervals in a transect from the front of the rock glacier to a position directly downvalley from the breach in the moraine. Coring was done in conjunction with a topographic survey, and with stratigraphic descriptions and sampling in 5 m of profile trench. The purpose of the study was to locate and identify clastic sediments that record the arrival of the rock glacier, and to bracket these sediments with radiocarbon dates. I also hoped to obtain dates for dissection of the moraine and for subsequent episodes of outwash deposition.

Description of the Transect. The transect can be conveniently divided into five sectors (Fig. 45), each with a different vegetation cover and depositional history.

A. *The Rock Glacier.* The front of the rock glacier is steep and unstable in its lower portions. Instability is due less to ongoing movement (for which there is little evidence) than to oversteepening by erosion where snow lies banked until mid summer. Turf-forming plant species such as *Dryas octopetala* and *Carex rupestris* grow above the level of late-lying snow (Fig. 46).

B. *Ground Moraine.* The front of the rock glacier rests on an apron of frost-sorted, bouldery ground moraine, which slopes at a low angle toward the bog. Large sorted nets, 3-6 m

Figure 44. Projectile point from profile locality 12. The point was not found *in situ*, but is believed to relate to the buried A1 horizon. Stem and base are unground; flaking is unpatterned; edge wear is absent. The point is 42 mm long, 24 mm wide, and 6.8 mm thick, with a hafting width of 18 mm.

in diameter, pattern the deposit; interconnected rock-filled channels carry meltwater across it. The diversity of rock types present, and the abundance of rounded and subrounded boulders, indicate that the deposit is glacial till; I have mapped it as an eroded outlier of late Pinedale ground moraine (Fig. 7). Angular talus boulders from the rock-glacier front are scattered across the surface of the till.

Vegetation is sparse due to late-lying snow and to local areas of continuing frost disturbance. Stable areas between boulders support soil lichens (*Lepraria arctica*), sedges (*Carex pyrenaica, C. nigricans*), rushes (*Juncus drummondii*), and mosses, the remains of which form a thin peat layer above brown, micaceous, silt loam subsoil.

C. *The* Carex nigricans *Meadow.* Between the apron of ground moraine and the pond, flanked on both sides by streams and seeps from the rock glacier, is a gently north-sloping sedge meadow (Fig. 46). The meadow supports an almost-pure stand of *Carex nigricans*, with a pond-shore fringe of *Carex scopulorum, Pedicularis groenlandica, Clementsia rhodantha,* and *Epilobium anagallidifolium.* Beneath the surface of the meadow there is a complex sequence of interbedded mucks, peats, and fine-textured micaceous clastic layers (Figs. 45, 47); the clastic layers slope away from the rock-glacier front and are believed to be derived from that source. Coarse-textured outwash gravels underlie the lowest organic sediments.

D. *The Pond.* The pond is small and shallow. It owes its formation, thousands of years ago, to impoundment of meltwater by debris flushed through the breach in the moraine and deposited along the axis of the valley. The locations of other ponds in the bog (Fig. 7) were also determined by this event. In autumn, as air temp-

54

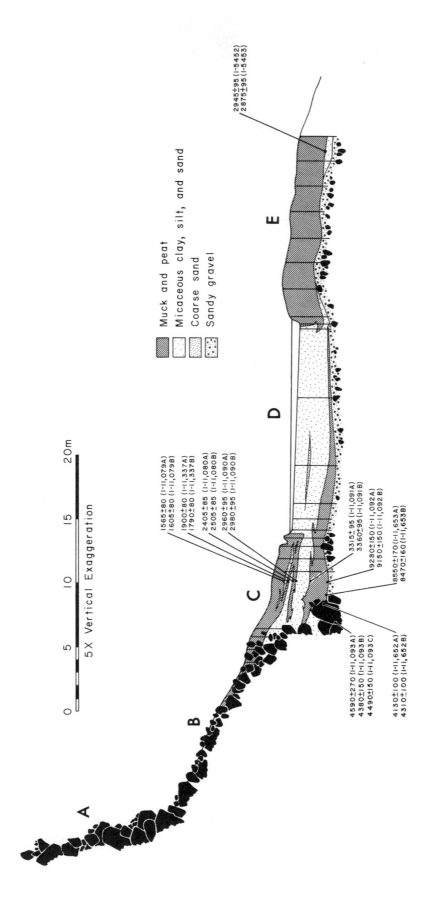

Figure 45. Topography and stratigraphy, Fourth of July Valley Bog. A, front of late Triple Lakes rock glacier; B, late Pinedale ground moraine; C, Carex nigricans meadow; D, pond; E, Carex scopulorum meadow. Vertical lines indicate coring locations; radio-carbon dates are from profile pits and trenches.

Figure 46. View of the rock-glacier front from the N shore of the pond, Fourth of July Valley Bog. A core is being taken from the *Carex nigricans* meadow at the location of figure 47. The juncture between the front and surface of the rock glacier is gradational and well vegetated, indicating that movement has essentially ceased at this locality (compare with figure 38). September 5, 1979.

eratures fall and meltwater production declines, the pond floor drains, but does not desiccate or crack.

The pond has maintained its present configuration for the past 3000 years, without encroachment by the sedge communities that grow along its shore (Fig. 45). A possible explanation is that late-lying snow has prohibited colonization by *Carex aquatilis*, an important pioneer species in shallow-water succession at timberline elevations. The shoreline of the pond may also have been affected from time to time by the pressure of expanding pond ice.

Coring revealed a surface layer of flocculent pond-floor sediments above a thick sequence of colorfully-laminated silts, clays, and sands, the finer facies of which were reduced and mottled, and the coarser facies strongly oxidized. These rested on a basal muck layer (Fig. 48), which thinned to a feather edge beneath the north shore of the pond. Coring was terminated by stony, gravelly outwash below the basal muck.

E. *The* Carex scopulorum *Meadow*. The pond is separated from the North Fork of Middle Boulder Creek by a gently north-sloping hummocky sedge meadow (Fig. 49). The meadow is richer in species and biomass than the *Carex nigricans* meadow because of a longer snow-free growing season. *Carex scopulorum* is the dominant peat-forming sedge; also important in

this plant community are *Caltha leptosepala*, *Trollius laxus*, *Carex nigricans*, *Deschampsia caespitosa*, *Ligusticum filicinum*, *Erigeron perigrinus*, *Swertia perennis*, and *Pedicularis groenlandica*, which grow from a spongy carpet of mosses. Coring and trenching (Figs. 45, 50) show that peat in this portion of the bog is relatively homogeneous. Streaks of silty muck are locally present, but discrete clastic layers do not occur. Their absence indicates that there has been no significant overbank flooding here during the past 3000 years, and that sediments from the rock glacier have not washed beyond the north shore of the pond. Coring below depths of 51-63 cm was prevented by stony, gravelly outwash, overlain near the stream by fine-textured micaceous outwash. Insofar as could be determined by coring, the topography of the contact between organic and inorganic sediments was parallel to the hummocky surface of the bog (Fig. 45).

Interpretation and Dating of the Clastic Layers. Nine potential sources exist for clastic deposits along the transect: (1) outwash from the early Satanta Peak glacier that deposited the moraine at site 5 BL 120; (2) outwash from a late Satanta Peak glacier that approached the site from the southwest, halting in the area now buried beneath the rock glacier (see Chapter 3); (3) till and late Satanta Peak outwash flushed into the bog during deglaciation, when the early Satanta Peak terminal mo-

56

Figure 47. Profile in the *Carex
nigricans* meadow. Light-colored
units are micaceous silts and
sands from the rock glacier; dark
units are mucks and peats; the
shovel rests on outwash gravels.
Note evidence of shearing from
south to north (left to right) at
the top of the lowermost organic
unit. Radiocarbon dates are for
the humin (top) and humic-acid
(bottom) fractions of 1-cm-thick
muck and peat samples.

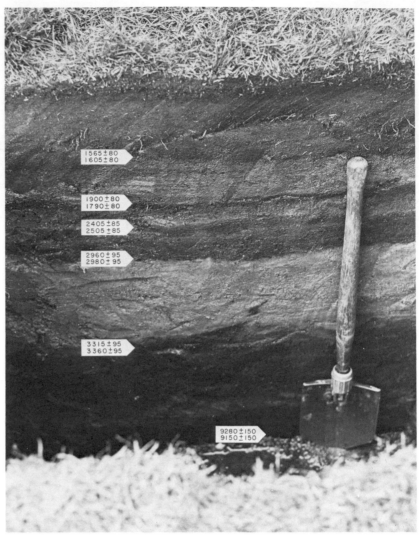

Figure 48. Core from the pond.
Depths are in centimeters below
the pond floor.

31-40 Strong brown (7.5YR 4/6 m)
         laminated sands, silts,
         and clays.
40-42 Dark gray (N4/ m) clay.
42-48 Very dark brown (10YR 2/3
         m) muck.
48-51 Dark gray (2.5Y 4/1 m)
         gravelly coarse sand.

Figure 49. View of the *Carex scopulorum* meadow, looking up-valley toward the early Satanta Peak terminal moraine. The N. Fork of Middle Boulder Creek crosses the moraine in a channel at the right side of the photograph; the Fourth of July Valley site (5 BL 120) is on the moraine crest at the front of the rock glacier. A shovel marks the location of the profile in figure 50. September 16, 1970.

Figure 50. Profile in the *Carex scopulorum* meadow. Sedge peat and mucky sedge peat overlie gray (5Y 5/1 m) sandy clay loam outwash. Radiocarbon dates are for the humin (top) and humic-acid (bottom) fractions of a 1-cm-thick basal peat sample.

2945±95
2875±95

58

raine was breached; (4) outwash from subsequent glacial advances, higher in the valley; (5) sediments shed by the rock glacier at times of active advance and/or frontal erosion; (6) sediments deposited by overbank flooding of the North Fork of Middle Boulder Creek, unrelated to glaciation; (7) sediments deposited as a result of local factors such as beaver activity; (8) windblown sand, silt, and clay; and (9) material eroded from surrounding hillslopes at times of increased snow cover.

Differences in the topography of unit boundaries, in the sorting and texture of clastic sediments, and in the roundness and lithology of clasts make it possible to distinguish between many of these potential sediment sources. The third, fourth, and fifth sources, in particular, are identifiable in the bog. The first and second are inferred to be present below the depth of coring and trenching. The eighth is not specifically identifiable, but is likely to be present as a component of the peat, if not as discrete layers.

Dating of clastic layers is based upon radiocarbon-age determinations for ten muck and peat samples (Fig. 45, Table 1). Dates for the humic acid (NaOH-soluble, HCl-insoluble) and humin (NaOH-insoluble) fractions of the samples agree closely, each be-

ing slightly older than the other in exactly half of the samples. To simplify discussion, I have averaged the dates using the method of Long and Rippeteau (1974).

Geologic History

Trenching of the Early Satanta Peak Moraine. The bog is floored with stony, gravelly, sandy outwash, which could not be penetrated with a peat corer, and was a conduit for groundwater that flooded profile trenches when intersected. The outwash is poorly sorted, and appears to have been deposited by a high-energy stream. Quartz pebbles and sand grains are frosted and rounded, indicating long-distance transport. The topography of the surface of the unit (Fig. 45) suggests deposition as a levee alongside the stream or as a fan with its apex at the gap in the early Satanta Peak moraine. Formation of the levee or fan is responsible for existence of the pond.

Because it is the uppermost coarse-textured clastic unit in the sequence of deposits, I attribute the outwash to the most recent high-energy hydrological event to affect the bog: i.e., breaching of the early Satanta Peak moraine, and dissection of the outwash plain behind it. Transport distances were short; pebbles and cobbles became rounded during a previous cycle of transportation and deposition. Average

LAB NO.	FRACTION	DATES	AVERAGE DATE
I-11,079A	Humin	1565 ± 80 BP	1585 ± 55 BP
I-11,079B	Humic acid	1605 ± 80 BP	
I-11,337A	Humin	1900 ± 80 BP	1845 ± 55 BP
I-11,337B	Humic acid	1790 ± 80 BP	
I-11,080A	Humin	2405 ± 85 BP	2455 ± 60 BP
I-11,080B	Humic acid	2505 ± 85 BP	
I-5452	Humin	2945 ± 95 BP	2910 ± 65 BP
I-5453	Humic acid	2875 ± 95 BP	
I-11,090A	Humin	2960 ± 95 BP	2970 ± 65 BP
I-11,090B	Humic acid	2980 ± 95 BP	
I-11,091A	Humin	3315 ± 95 BP	3340 ± 65 BP
I-11,091B	Humic acid	3360 ± 95 BP	
I-11,652A	Humic acid	4130 ± 100 BP	4220 ± 70 BP
I-11,652B	Humin	4310 ± 100 BP	
I-11,093A	Humin	4590 ± 270 BP	
I-11,093B	Humic acid	4380 ± 150 BP	4455 ± 100 BP
I-11,093C	Humin	4490 ± 150 BP	
I-11,653A	Humic acid	8550 ± 170 BP	8505 ± 115 BP
I-11,653B	Humin	8470 ± 160 BP	
I-11,092A	Humin	9280 ± 150 BP	9215 ± 105 BP
I-11,092B	Humic acid	9150 ± 150 BP	

Table 1. Weighted average dates for muck and peat samples from the Fourth of July Valley Bog. Sample locations are shown in figure 45.

dates of 9215 ± 105 BP and 8505 ± 115 BP for ½-cm-thick basal muck samples collected directly above the sandy gravel provide minimum ages for Satanta Peak deglaciation.

Backwater Ponding. Deposition of the basal outwash was followed by a lengthy interval of shallow ponding, during which virtually no clastic material entered the bog. Muck accumulated at an average rate of 5-6 mm per ^{14}C century, approximately one-third the modern rate of peat accumulation in the *C. scopulorum* meadow. Standing water is indicated by the leaves and perigynia of *C. aquatilis*, a sedge that does not presently grow in the pond despite water depths comparable to those in nearby ponds where the species is abundant. A possible explanation for its absence in the pond today is the abbreviated growing season, caused by late-lying snow at the front of the rock glacier.

The presence of *C. aquatilis* and the near-absence of clastic sedimentation between 9215 ± 105 BP and 3340 ± 65 BP suggest that the rock glacier that now stands at the southern margin of the bog had not yet come close enough to disrupt snow-accumulation patterns or supply sand to the pond floor.

Tree Growth and Patterned-Ground Activity. Till boulders deep beneath the southern edge of the *C. nigricans* meadow (Fig. 45) are the subsurface expression of patterned ground that is exposed at the surface a few meters

to the west (Fig. 51). Interstices between the boulders are filled with angular gravel and with well-preserved organic detritus, identified by Richard G. Baker (pers. comm. 1980) as consisting of *Picea* and *Abies* needles and cone scales, intact *Picea* cones, leaves (cf. Ericaceae), seeds (cf. *Vaccinium, Juncus*), and fruits (*Potentilla gracilis* type, *Carex* cf. *nigricans*). The average ages of two litter samples were 4455 ± 100 and 4220 ± 70 radiocarbon years. Similar concentrations of litter (but *without* spruce cones) can be found today between stones in the borders of sorted nets near the rock-glacier front.

Spruce cones (Fig. 52) accounted for 10-20% of the volume of both litter samples collected for radiocarbon dating. Such high concentrations occur in the valley today only (1) directly beneath cone-bearing spruce trees and (2) in ponds and snow-accumulation areas immediately downwind from such trees (where the cones are concentrated by wind, currents, and snowmelt processes). Cones in the bog must therefore have accumulated at a time when trees grew close to the sampling locality, probably to the west. The only nearby locality that is well-enough drained for tree growth is the crest of the early Satanta Peak moraine at site 5 BL 120. This sector of the moraine is treeless today, due to late-lying snow deposited in a backeddy, or "rotor", at the front of the rock glacier. The presence of cone-bearing trees *ca.* 4455 ± 100 and 4220 ± 70 radiocarbon years ago indicates that the rock glacier had

Figure 51. View of the *Carex nigricans* meadow, Fourth of July Valley Bog. Spruce cones at 84- to 118-cm depth in openwork rubble beneath the packframe are thought to have washed there through the borders of frost patterns such as the sorted net in the foreground. Average dates of 4455 ± 100 and 4220 ± 70 BP apply to a time when cone-bearing spruce trees grew on the moraine west of the sample locality. September 29, 1980.

Figure 52. Spruce cone (*Picea engelmannii*) from the Fourth of July Valley Bog (left). A modern cone is illustrated for comparison (right). The fossil cone was found at 113- to 118-cm depth in an accumulation of forest litter dated at 4455 ± 100 radiocarbon years BP.

not yet come close enough to this locality to modify snow-accumulation patterns.

The mechanism by which spruce cones became incorporated in patterned-ground borders that were sealed from the surface by undisturbed bog sediments is not entirely clear. Most probably, the cones blew and/or washed into the borders of nearby patterns that remained open at the surface (Fig. 51), then filtered downward and laterally through interstices between the stones. The difficulty comes in explaining why their accumulation was episodic, rather than continuous during mid-postglacial time. One of several possible explanations is that patterned ground in the till apron was reactivated between 4500 and 4000 yr BP, and that shifting of stones in the borders of the patterns facilitated downward movement of the plant detritus.

Deposition of Late Triple Lakes Outwash. At the north end of the transect, a few meters from the stream (Figs. 45, 50), bouldery outwash is overlain by gray, micaceous, sandy clay loam outwash. The origin of the unit is uncertain. To reach this locality, sediments from the rock glacier would have had to by-pass an intervening low ridge of coarse-textured material. A simpler explanation is that the deposit is outwash from late Triple Lakes glaciers or rock glaciers higher in the valley. Regardless of its origin, the deposit is older than 2910 ± 65 radiocarbon years, the mean age of a 1-cm-thick basal peat sample collected directly above it.

Arrival of the Rock Glacier. The most distinctive stratigraphic unit in the sequence of deposits beneath the present *C. nigricans* meadow is a thick layer of dark greenish gray (5GY 4/1 m) to dark gray (2.5Y 4/ m) biotite-rich silt and clay, containing thin, unmappable sand lenses. The largest clastic particles are 3-4 mm in maximum dimension. The lower 1-3 cm of the unit is stained with humus eroded from underlying muck and peat; the contact between the two deposits suggests shearing (Figs. 45, 47), and indicates that the radiocarbon age of peat collected directly below the contact may overrepresent the age of the silt-clay layer.

Several factors suggest that the silt, clay, and sand have washed from the front of the rock glacier: (1) the unit slopes from

	ANGULAR	SUBANGULAR	SUBROUNDED	ROUNDED
Basal Outwash	4%	44%	44%	8%
Outwash from the Rock Glacier	57%	36%	7%	0%

Table 2. Rounding of coarse sand grains in clastic deposits, Fourth of July Valley Bog.

south to north, from the rock glacier toward
the pond; (2) shearing at the base of the
unit implies movement of sediments from south
to north; (3) small pebbles and coarse sand
grains are predominantly angular (Table 2),
suggesting a short transport distance; and
(4) outwash from the rock glacier accumulated
on the moraine at site 5 BL 120 (units C-7,
D-3, Chapter 3), and could not have done so
without also spilling into the bog.

I interpret the sudden shift from organic to clastic sedimentation soon after 3340 ±
65 BP as evidence that the rock glacier had
arrived at the southern edge of the bog. The
rock glacier remained active until *ca.* 2970 ±
65 BP. Agreement is good with a lichenometric
age of 3150 yr obtained for this lobe of the
rock-glacier complex, and with other age evidence discussed on pp. 48-49. However, neither the radiocarbon nor the lichenometric
dates necessarily apply to rock-glacier *ori-
gen*: they may instead date the advance of a
previously-existing rock glacier to a position close to its present location.

Rock-Glacier Reactivation. Layers of clay,
silt, and biotite-rich sand higher in the sequence of deposits beneath the *C. nigricans*
meadow (Fig. 47) are thinner and less-clearly
defined. Gravel and coarse sand are absent;
organic matter is relatively abundant. The
clastic layers slope to the north, away from
the rock glacier, but do not extend to the
shore of the pond. Because they are absent in
the *C. scopulorum* meadow, beyond the pond
(Fig. 50), loessal and overbank-flooding origins can be excluded.

The slopes and locations of the clastic
layers, and the angularity of their fine sand
grains, suggest derivation from the front of
the rock glacier; it is uncertain whether
they indicate times of renewed advance, or
times when the vegetation cover of the rock-
glacier front was weakened by an expanded
snowcover, facilitating erosion. In either
case, they are likely to relate to the snowbank-expansion intervals of Audubon time.

Average radiocarbon ages of 2455 ± 60 BP
and 1845 ± 55 BP bracket the initial period
of rock-glacier reactivation (Fig. 47). Average dates of 1845 ± 55 BP and 1585 ± 55 BP
bracket deposition of a thicker clastic layer,
thought to indicate a more-important period
of rock-glacier activity. A third, and minor,
episode of rock-glacier activity is suggested
by increased sandiness at depths of 6 to 13
cm in the muck/peat sequence.

Radiocarbon dates for the two principal
periods of rock-glacier reactivation agree
closely with lichenometric dates of 1900 to
1600 yr BP for emergence of the valley floor
from beneath late-lying snow. Snowbanks are
likely to have persisted in topographic lows
during the final, minor, period of reactivation.

3 Excavations at the Fourth of July Valley Site (5BL120)

Introduction

The Fourth of July Valley site (5 BL 120) is a single-component hunting camp on the outer of two Satanta Peak terminal moraines in the Fourth of July valley study area (Figs. 13, 53). Its coordinates are 40°00'25" north latitude, 105°40'14" west longitude. The site is in the forest-tundra ecotone, at an altitude of 3415 m. Clumps of flagged spruce and fir trees grow on the moraine crest north of the stream; only tundra vegetation is present in the occupation area, to the south.

The site was discovered and briefly reported by W.F. Husted (1965: 494-496), who visited it annually during the early 1960s to collect cultural material eroding from the inner slope of the moraine. I excavated a 41 m² area at the site in 1971; my purpose was to investigate the association of obliquely-flaked stemmed and lanceolate projectile points in Husted's surface collection, and to obtain radiocarbon dates that would assist in interpreting the sequence of multiple moraines and rock glaciers in the vicinity. A preliminary summary (Benedict and Olson 1973) emphasized projectile-point typology; this chapter is a final report on excavations.

slopes to the modern floodplain and to a shallow, ponded section of the stream (Fig. 53). South of the excavation area, a late Triple Lakes lobate rock glacier towers 14 m above the moraine crest.

Proximity of the rock glacier has affected the site in several ways. For much of the summer, snow lies banked against its bouldery front (Fig. 55), limiting the interval suitable for habitation to about 2 months, on average, and providing meltwater to fuel a variety of geological processes. Fine-textured outwash sediments in the area of latest-lying snow are sparsely vegetated and eroded (Fig. 54); this is the "coarse sand of decomposed granite" in which Husted (1965) made his original surface discoveries. If there were no rock glacier at the southern margin of the site, snow accumulation would be shallower, the summer snow-free season would be at least a month longer, the stratigraphic sequence would be less complex, and the site would probably never have been discovered.

Environment

The occupation area is at the southern end of the moraine crest, where a small, level clearing, roughly circular in outline, interrupts the otherwise-bouldery surface of the moraine (Fig. 54). A late-snowbed community of *Lepraria arctica*, *Sibbaldia procumbens*, *Vaccinium scoparium*, *Carex nigricans*, *Erigeron melanocephalus*, and mosses grows in the clearing. East of the site, the moraine slopes steeply to the Fourth of July Valley Bog; westward, it

Field Procedures

We excavated the Fourth of July Valley site in August and early September, 1971. A grid system of 1 m × 1 m squares (Fig. 56 a) was laid out west-southwestward from the moraine crest, in the direction of steepest slope. Troweling by natural stratigraphic units resulted in recovery of most chipped-stone tools and waste flakes (Figs. 56 b, c) in clear-cut stratigraphic context; a small amount of additional material was found in screening. Units containing loessal silt were wet-sieved at the site.

Figure 53. View of the Fourth of July Valley site (5 BL 120), looking east. An arrow points to the excavation area, on the crest and inner slope of the early Satanta Peak terminal moraine. A late Triple Lakes rock glacier stands at the south margin of the site; bare soil at its front is the result of late-lying snow. Behind the moraine is the Fourth of July Valley Bog; in the foreground, outwash terraces of late Satanta Peak age flank the North Fork of Middle Boulder Creek. September 6, 1974.

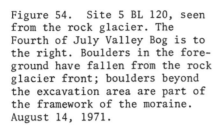

Figure 54. Site 5 BL 120, seen from the rock glacier. The Fourth of July Valley Bog is to the right. Boulders in the foreground have fallen from the rock glacier front; boulders beyond the excavation area are part of the framework of the moraine. August 14, 1971.

Figure 55. Mid-summer view of the Fourth of July Valley site. The man is standing on 1-2 m of snow, directly above the excavation area. July 16, 1979.

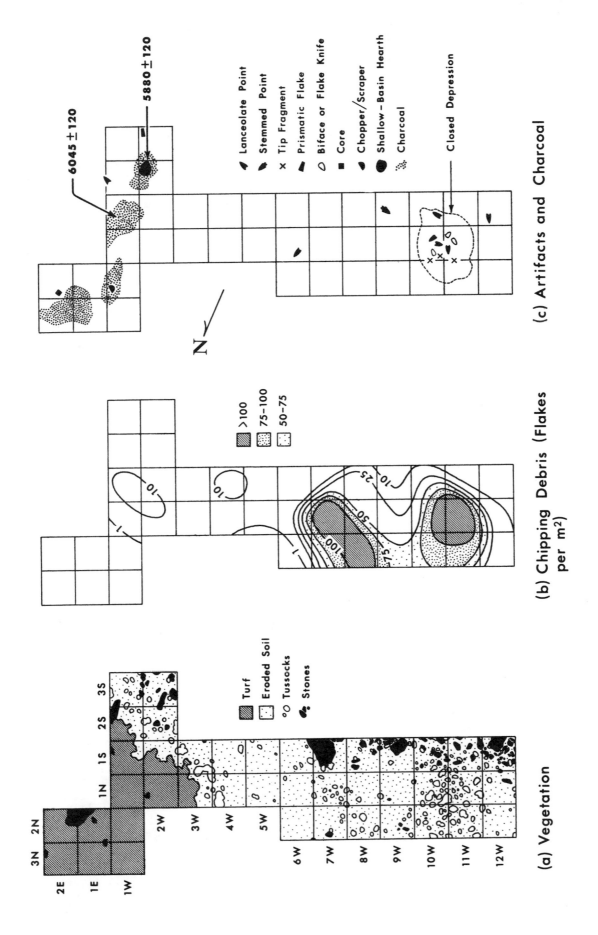

6045 ± 120

5880 ± 120

Lanceolate Point
Stemmed Point
× Tip Fragment
Prismatic Flake
Biface or Flake Knife
Core
Chopper/Scraper
Shallow-Basin Hearth
Charcoal
Closed Depression

N

(c) Artifacts and Charcoal

>100
75-100
50-75

(b) Chipping Debris (Flakes per m²)

Turf
Eroded Soil
Tussocks
Stones

(a) Vegetation

Figure 56. Maps of the excavation area, site 5 BL 120. Note the correlation between rush-tussock density, chipping-debris distribution, and artifact oc-currence in the southern part of the excavation area.

Stratigraphy and Geologic History

INTRODUCTION

Early hunters were attracted to the Fourth of July Valley site by its view of the surrounding countrysite (still unobstructed by the rock glacier), and by its level, well-drained, vegetated surface (Fig. 54). The meadow clearing exists because a succession of geological processes have supplied fine-textured sediments to the moraine crest at this locality, burying till boulders that would otherwise have discouraged human use. Included in the blanketing deposits are proglacial lake silts, stratified outwash sands and gravels, colluvium, slopewash sediments, and loess.

All parts of the site have experienced erosion during the past; some are experiencing it today. Erosion has been least on the crest of the moraine, north of the area affected by nivation; here the tundra-meadow vegetation is unbroken, and a thin turf horizon has developed. This is the only part of the site in which cultural material remains in its original stratigraphic context except for minor up-freezing of artifacts. A profile from this part of the excavation area (Figs. 57, 58) is important because it tells us *when*, in the sequence of geological events, the site was occupied, and because of the information it provides about former episodes of loess deposition.

At the opposite end of the disturbance spectrum is the profile in figure 59, described at a mid-slope location. Here snow is persistent, vegetation is absent, needle ice is an important erosive agent, and the upper 10-20 cm of soil are in slow downslope transit due to frost-creep processes. This profile is important because of the data it provides about former lake levels, the ice core of the moraine, and outwash deformation.

Figures 60-62 are profiles from the lower slope of the moraine, where tussocks of *Juncus drummondii* are recolonizing the bare gravel surface. Chipped-stone implements were recovered in large numbers from redeposited loess filling a natural basin at this locality; underlying deposits record the advance, retreat, and readvance of Satanta Peak glaciers in the valley, the lateral excursions of the North Fork of Middle Boulder Creek on its high outwash plain, and the arrival of the rock glacier at the southern margin of the site.

Interpretation of the depositional and erosional history of the moraine is based on profile drawings and descriptions (Figs. 58-59, 61-62), laboratory analyses (Figs. 63-64), and excavation notes. I have attempted to relate stratigraphic units and erosion surfaces at the site to the sequence of late Quaternary events recognized elsewhere in the study area (Chapter 2), and particularly to the radiocarbon chronology of the Fourth of July Valley Bog, which has received sediments from several of the same sources as the occupation area. A generalized correlation chart is given in figure 65.

DEPOSITION OF THE MORAINE

The deepest sediments encountered in the excavation area are glacial till, represented in figures 57-62 by boulders at the bottom of each profile. The matrix of the upper part of the till is gone, flushed from the site by water flowing across the moraine crest, or slumped into deep voids left by melting glacial ice[14]. The voids are filled with lake sediments, beach sands, and outwash. Till boulders are subangular to subrounded, and show no evidence of weathering attributable to subaerial exposure. Thin (1-2 mm) coatings of silt and clay on the upper surfaces of boulders reflect downward migration of fines due to vertical frost sorting (Corte 1963), or to downwash during thaw (Harris and Ellis 1980). The moraine was deposited by the first of two Satanta Peak glacial advances to enter the study area (Chapter 2).

DEPOSITION OF BEACH AND/OR OUTWASH SANDS AND GRAVELS

West of the moraine crest, patches of loose, poorly-sorted, olive (5Y 4/3 m) to olive brown (2.5Y 4/3 m) gravelly coarse sand (unit B-1) and well-sorted gravel-free fine sandy loam (unit C-1) are perched atop till boulders, or form a matrix between them. Because of the wide range of erosional and depositional processes that can modify the surfaces of newly-deposited moraines, such small exposures cannot be adequately interpreted. Good sorting, sandy texture, and a conformable relationship to overlying lake silts may indicate that unit C-1 is a beach or nearshore lake deposit; unit B-1 may be of glaciofluvial origin.

DEPOSITION OF PROGLACIAL LAKE SILTS AND SANDS

Lake sediments more than 90 cm thick occur on the inner slope of the moraine, forming a wedge that thins upslope, disappearing a short distance west of the moraine crest. The uppermost lake sediments are only 10 cm lower than the tops of the highest till boulders in the excavation area, suggesting that the excavation area was a spillway, or more probably a shallow embayment, when the lake stood at its highest level; because of the fine texture of the lake sediments, discharge through the occupation area cannot have been large.

---

[14] *North of the excavation area the till matrix is an indurated, stony, very gravelly sandy loam, light olive brown (2.5Y 5/3 m) in color (Fig. 24).*

The lake deposits (units B-2, C-2, and D-1) are uniformly well sorted, with a loam, silt loam, or silty clay loam texture (Fig. 64, samples 4644, 4645, 4652). Shades of olive (5Y 5/3-5/4 m), olive gray (5Y 4/2 m), and light olive brown (2.5Y 5/3-5/5 m) predominate; strong brown and yellowish red mottles in the upper part of the deposit reflect fluctuating moisture conditions. The sediments are cohesive, fissile, and finely laminated, although not varved. Thin lenses of medium to fine sand trend approximately parallel to the original upper surface of the deposit. The sand lenses are loose and structureless, and tend to be more strongly oxidized than the fine-textured material that surrounds them. Some are well sorted; others are poorly sorted, and contain pebbles as large as 5 mm. Widely scattered erratic pebbles, cobbles, and small boulders in the lake silts are thought to have been rafted to their present positions by floating ice.

A radiocarbon age of 7220 ± 310 BP (I-11,128A) was obtained for lake silts and clays in the north wall of grid square 1N/10W (Fig. 61). The sample was collected between till (below) and outwash (above), and was expected to date the non-glacial interval separating the ice advances of early and late Satanta Peak time. The <125 μ NaOH-insoluble fraction of the sample was dated, as recommended by Stuckenrath et al. (1979). Insufficient NaOH-soluble, HCl-insoluble material was obtained for a companion date.

The date, if reliable, would indicate that outwash gravels on the crest and inner slope of the moraine are younger than 7220 ± 310 radiocarbon years (the age of carbon in lake sedi-

Figure 57. North wall, grid square 1S/1W. Charcoal from an open fireplace, dated at 6045 ± 120 BP (I-6545), marks the occupation surface, which is overlain by humus-rich loess. Fine-textured sediments beneath the occupation surface contain silt from an earlier episode of loess deposition. Sands and pebble gravels are late Satanta Peak outwash. The trowel rests on a till boulder, 65-70 cm below ground surface.

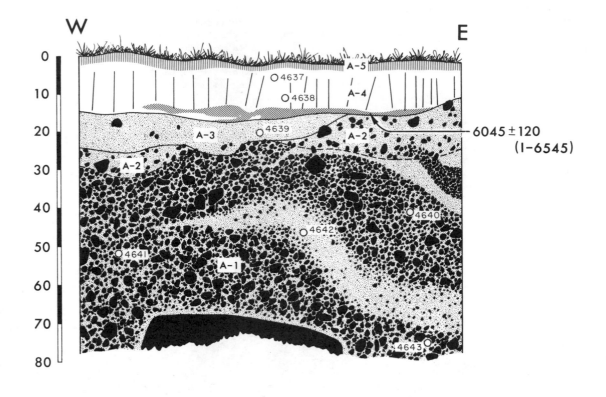

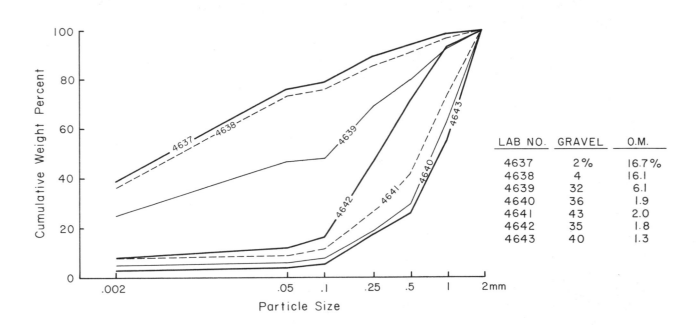

LAB NO.	GRAVEL	O.M.
4637	2%	16.7%
4638	4	16.1
4639	32	6.1
4640	36	1.9
4641	43	2.0
4642	35	1.8
4643	40	1.3

Figure 58. Profile drawing and laboratory data, north wall of grid square 1S/1W. Soil-sample locations are shown with open circles and Colorado State University Soil Testing Laboratory lab numbers. Vertical lines in unit A-4 are mudcracks; diagonal hatching shows the distribution of charcoal. Figure 57 is a photograph of the same profile.

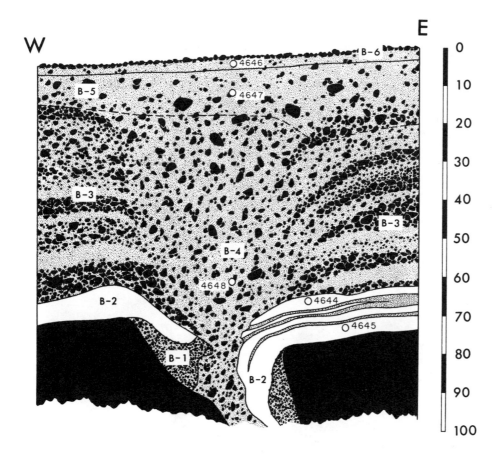

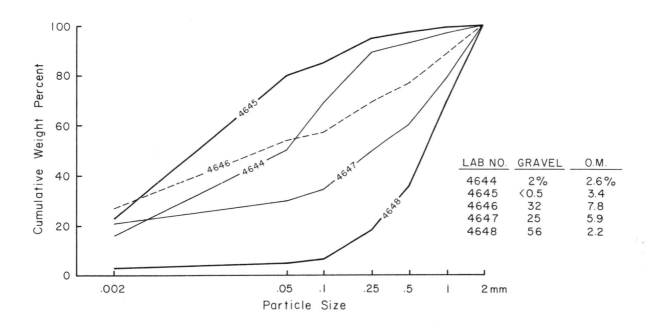

LAB NO.	GRAVEL	O.M.
4644	2%	2.6%
4645	<0.5	3.4
4646	32	7.8
4647	25	5.9
4648	56	2.2

Figure 59. Profile drawing and laboratory data, north wall of grid square 1S/5W. Downwarping of proglacial lake sediments (unit B-2) and outwash (unit B-3) above gap between till boulders at base of profile is attributed to melting of interstitial ice. Stratification in unit B-4 has been obliterated by slumping. Units B-5 and B-6 are mass-wasting deposits.

Figure 60. North wall, grid squares 1N/11W and 1N/10W. Till boulders are overlain by proglacial lake silts, horizontally-bedded outwash sands and gravels (extreme right), two colluvial units, oxidized slopewash sediments (left side), dark, humus-rich redeposited loess, and gravelly mass-wasting sediments. The marker peg is graduated in inches. Debris behind the rush tussocks is part of the back-dirt pile.

Figure 61 (facing page). Profile drawing and laboratory data, north wall, grid squares 1N/11W and 1N/10W. Note the conformable relationship between stratified outwash (unit C-3) and underlying lake sediments (unit C-2); the erosion surface and scarp cut by the North Fork of Middle Boulder Creek (heavy line); and the relationship between colluvial units C-5 (oldest) and C-8 (youngest). The radiocarbon age is considered to be several thousand years too young (see text). Figure 60 is a photograph of the same profile.

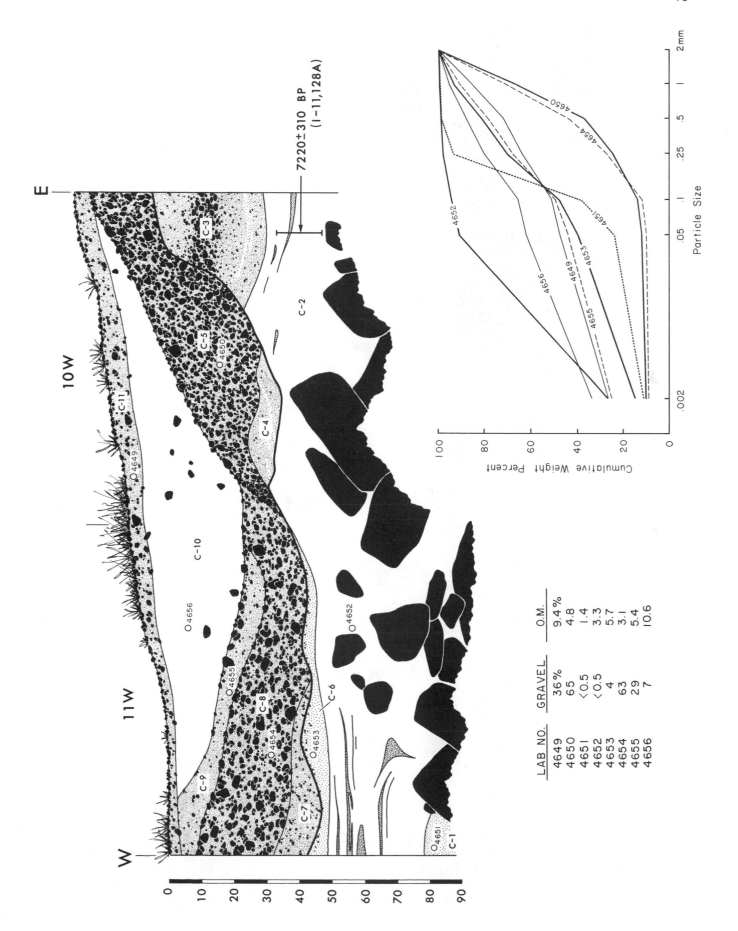

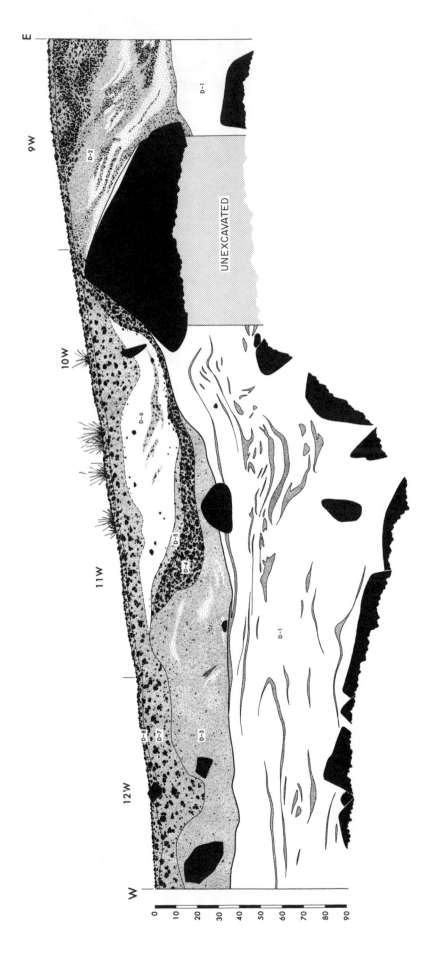

Figure 62. Profile drawing, south wall of grid squares 1N/12W, 1N/11W, 1N/10W, and 1N/9W. Unit D-3, a sand deposit containing angular boulders, is thought to mark the arrival of the rock glacier at the southern margin of the site, and to be equivalent in age both to fine-textured outwash in the "sand ridge" (Fig. 43) and to the principal layer of clastic sediments in the Fourth of July Valley Bog (Fig. 47).

ments beneath them), and older than 5960 ± 85 radiocarbon years (the average age of occupational charcoal above them). Outwash, however, could *not* have been deposited on the crest of the moraine without spilling over into the Fourth of July Valley Bog, directly to the east; excavations in the bog (Chapter 2) show that organic sediments accumulated without interruption between 9215 ± 105 BP and 3340 ± 65 BP. There are no outwash gravels in this portion of the bog sequence; hence no outwash can have been deposited on the moraine crest during this time interval; hence the lake-sediment date must be at least 2000 years too young.

An error due to contamination is not surprising, considering the low organic-matter content of the sample. Approximately 10 kg of material were submitted to Teledyne Isotopes; combustion produced only 0.6 g of carbon, and dilution was required in order to fill a low-volume counter (James Buckley, pers. comm. 1980). There were no visible contaminants; however, even a very small increment of modern organic matter might significantly affect the radiocarbon age of a sample with such minuscule amounts of original carbon (Olsson 1974, Fig. 2). Contamination by modern rootlets is likely to be a particular problem at sites such as 5 BL 120, on the floor of a late-lying snowbank, due to the high concentration of fallout radionuclides (Osburn 1963, 1966, pers. comm. 1979).

OUTWASH DEPOSITION

Bedded outwash sands and gravels (units A-1, B-3, C-3, and D-2) rest conformably upon the lake sediments. Individual outwash strata range from pebble gravels to sands, gravelly sands, and gravelly loamy sands (Fig. 64, samples 4640-43, 4648). Pebbles are subangular to rounded, with long-axis orientations parallel to stratification; the largest pebble is 7 cm in maximum dimension. Sorting ranges from moderate to good. Colors vary with differences in texture and permeability and with position relative to the water table and to an oxidation profile developed during soil formation. 10YR, 7.5YR, and 5YR hues are characteristic of the coarsest strata, which are loose and structureless; 2.5Y hues occur in firmer, siltier units and at depths greater than 50-60 cm below modern ground surface on the moraine crest. Very strongly oxidized (5YR 4/4-4/8 m) sands and fine gravels deep within the outwash are thought to reflect contact with oxygenated groundwater.

The conformable relationship of outwash sands and gravels to underlying lake sediments suggests deposition as part of an uninterrupted cycle of glacier advance, retreat, and readvance during Satanta Peak time. For reasons discussed in chapter 2 (pp. 58-59), the cycle is thought to have ended prior to 9215 ± 105 BP (I-11,092).

Two factors distinguish outwash in the excavation area from outwash in high terraces along the North Fork of Middle Boulder Creek: (1) the largest stream-transported clasts in the excavation area are an order of magnitude smaller than clasts in the terraces; and (2) the upper surface of outwash on the crest of the moraine is 0.6 m higher than the projected elevation of terraces flanking the stream, despite subsidence due to ice-core melting at the former locality.

These differences are attributed to deposition by streams with different sources, discharges, and hydrologic histories, rather than to differences in age. Terraces along the North Fork of Middle Boulder Creek were strongly influenced by events in the upper valley, as indicated by the presence of Silver Plume granite erratics. Swollen by meltwater from glaciers in the Neva cirques, the North Fork was able to transport boulder-sized material over a floodplain with a gentle (1°-2°) gradient. In contrast, gravels in the excavation area were deposited as part of the outwash apron of a late Satanta Peak glacier that terminated just south of the site, beneath the present rock glacier. The north-facing orientation of the glacier discouraged meltwater production, limiting the maximum size of material that could be transported.

LATERAL EROSION BY THE NORTH FORK OF MIDDLE BOULDER CREEK

Outwash terraces west of the site are graded to the altitude of a shallow, flat-floored notch in the moraine crest, directly north of the present outlet stream (Fig. 27, profile A-A'). The floodplain that existed at this time is recorded in the excavation area by a buried erosion surface and scarp cut in Satanta Peak lake sediments and outwash (Figs. 60-61). The scarp is 30 to 40 cm high, and appears to have formed in two stages, separated by a slight (*ca.* 10 cm) lowering of base level. Patches of sandy outwash (unit C-4) may have accumulated on the floodplain during the interim. The base of the scarp is 1.4 to 1.5 m below benchmark A, installed in the moraine crest at profile locality 2 (Fig. 13), and coincides with the projected elevation of high outwash-terrace remnants along the North Fork of Middle Boulder Creek.

MELTING OF ICE IN THE MORAINE CORE

Bedding planes in outwash on the crest and upper slopes of the moraine bend steeply downward as they cross the gaps between underlying till boulders (Fig. 59). All traces of primary bedding are obliterated in funnel-shaped zones of disturbed outwash sediments directly above each opening (unit B-4). The disturbed sediments are dark yellowish brown (10YR 4/4 m) in color, changing to olive brown (2.5Y 4/4 m) about 80-90 cm below the present ground surface. Pebbles show no preferred orientation. Deformation of the outwash is thought to have occurred during an interval of relatively warm climate, when interstitial ice melted from the framework of erratic boulders. Survival of early Satanta Peak ice until the end of late Satanta Peak time suggests that the intervening non-glacial interval was brief, and not particularly warm. Because

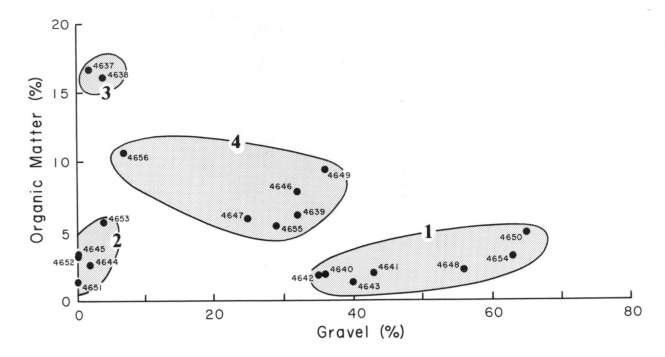

Figure 63. Gravel and organic-matter content, Fourth of July Valley site. *1*, outwash and colluvium; *2*, lake and beach (?) sediments; *3*, loess; *4*, slopewash and mass-wasting deposits. Sample locations are shown in figures 58, 59, and 61.

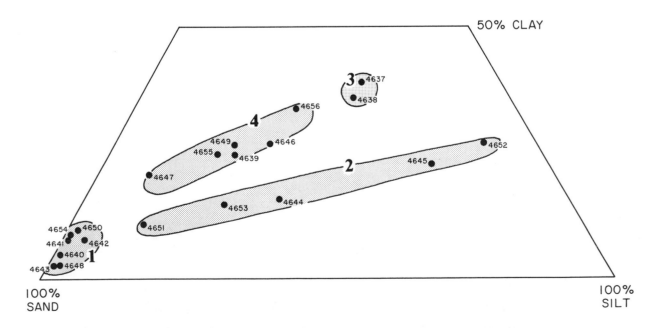

Figure 64. Triangular diagram showing textural analyses from the Fourth of July Valley site. *1*, outwash and colluvium; *2*, lake and beach (?) sediments; *3*, loess; *4*, slopewash and mass-wasting deposits. Sample locations are shown in figures 58, 59, and 61.

the occupation surface (Figs. 57, 58) shows
no evidence of deformation, ice must have disappeared completely from the moraine by 5960
± 85 radiocarbon years ago.

DEPOSITION OF COLLUVIAL AND SLOPEWASH SEDIMENTS

Unit C-5, on the lower slope of the moraine (Figs. 60, 61), is a loose and poorly-
sorted colluvial deposit, similar in texture
(Fig. 64) to the outwash from which it was
derived. The deposit is dark brown (7.5YR 3/4
m) to strong brown (7.5YR 3/6 m) in color.
Pebbles are subangular to rounded, and are
similar in maximum dimension to pebbles in
coarse outwash units higher on the slope;
the largest pebbles are underlain by thin layers of frost-sorted coarse sand and fine gravel. There is no visible preferred orientation. The deposit is a result of slumping and
mass-wasting across the scarp cut by the North
Fork of Middle Boulder Creek, and is absent,
or poorly developed, where soil-movement processes were obstructed by the damming effect
of large till boulders (Fig. 62). A scarcity
of silt and clay in the colluvium indicates
deposition soon after scarp development, before significant quantities of loess had accumulated on the moraine surface[15].

West of the lobe of colluvium, beyond its
front, a thin layer of strong brown (7.5YR 4/6
m) fine sandy loam (unit C-6) occurs at the
eroded surface of the lake sediments. The unit
is coarser textured than *in situ* lake silts
and clays, and is less well sorted, more
strongly oxidized, and richer in organic matter (Figs. 63, 64, sample 4653). I interpret
it as a disturbed facies of the lake deposit,
containing an admixture of debris washed from
the colluvium. Oxidation and humus enrichment
reflect (1) *in situ* soil formation, or (2)
erosion and redeposition of material from an
older soil, higher on the moraine. In either
case, an interval of subaerial exposure is im-
plied.

LOESS DEPOSITION AND REWORKING

Stratigraphic units A-2 and A-3 (Figs.
57, 58) record deposition and reworking of
windblown silt on the crest of the moraine.
Unit A-2 is a stony, gravelly sandy loam or
sandy clay loam with moderate blocky structure and fine (*ca.* 1 mm) spherical vesicles.
It consists of frost-disturbed outwash with a
generous admixture of loess. Unit A-3 is a
loess-rich gravelly sandy clay loam slopewash
deposit, which has accumulated in depressions
in the outwash surface. Neither deposit contains cultural material; both predate occupa-

tion of the site. Dark yellowish brown (10YR
4/5-4/8 m) colors reflect B-horizon oxidation,
probably (but not necessarily) *in situ*.

OCCUPATION

The occupation surface, on the moraine
crest, is marked by thick, discontinuous concentrations of charcoal that rest on reworked
outwash and slopewash sediments (Figs. 57, 58).
Where the charcoal is underlain by silty material a 3- to 4-mm-thick oxidized zone, yellowish red (5YR 3/6 m) in color, indicates
that it burned in place. No visible oxidation
occurs where the charcoal is underlain by gravelly debris.

Two radiocarbon dates were obtained for
occupation. An irregular concentration of charcoal on the eroded surface of stratigraphic
units A-2 and A-3 in grid square 1S/1W (Figs.
56 c, 57, 58) was dated at 6045 ± 120 BP (I-
6545). Small quartzite flakes, discolored by
heat, occurred in the charcoal and immediately
above it. The charcoal was overlain by 12 to
16 cm of loess.

A shallow-basin hearth in the southeast
corner of grid square 2S/2W (Fig. 56 c) contained charcoal with a radiocarbon age of 5880
± 120 yr (I-6544). The hearth was irregularly
oval in plan view, with maximum and minimum
diameters of 45 and 33 cm. It originated at
the surface of slopewash unit A-3, and was 9 cm
deep; its fill of charcoal and charcoal-stained
sandy soil was overlain by 8-9 cm of loess.
Sediments beneath the hearth were oxidized yellowish red (5YR 3/8 m) to a depth of 3 mm. The
basin was neither lined nor filled with stones,
and contained no artifacts, bone scrap, or
chipping debris. However, burned flakes of chert
and chalcedony occurred in the immediate vicinity.

Both charcoal samples are believed to have
resulted from a single visit to the site. Their
average age is 5960 ± 85 radiocarbon years.

The occupation area gives every indication
of having been an attractive campsite 5960 [14]C
yr ago. Boulders had by this time become deeply
buried beneath outwash sands and gravels, and
depressions caused by ice-core melting had become filled with loess-rich slopewash sediments,
producing a smooth surface. The North Fork of
Middle Boulder Creek had dissected its former
high floodplain into well-drained terraces that
provided space for activities that could not be
accommodated in the small clearing at 5 BL 120;
site 5 BL 169 (Fig. 13) is a possible candidate
for such overflow activities. Because the rock
glacier had not yet advanced to the edge of the
site, winter snowdrift patterns were different
than they are today, and the summer snow-free
season was longer. Spruce and fir trees (present at or near the site as long ago as 4455 ±
100 radiocarbon years) are likely to have been
present during occupation, although this is not
certain.

Regional climatic conditions were warm and
relatively dry (Benedict 1979a). Occupation coincided with an interval of widespread soil
formation above timberline in the Indian Peaks

---

[15] *Loess was deposited at profile locality 6, a
short distance to the southwest, prior to
8270 ± 140 radiocarbon yr BP (I-11,127, Fig.
30). This can probably be taken as a minimum
age for colluvial unit C-5.*

76

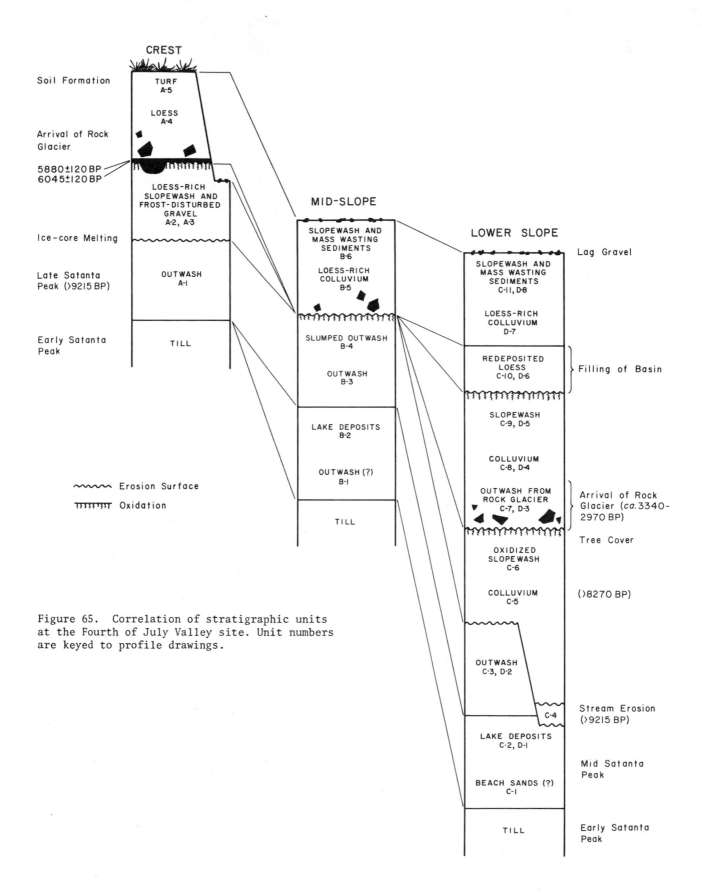

Figure 65. Correlation of stratigraphic units at the Fourth of July Valley site. Unit numbers are keyed to profile drawings.

(Benedict and Olson 1978, Burns 1979); this interval is recorded in the Fourth of July valley by a radiocarbon age of 5910 ± 115 BP (I-11,370A) for redeposited soil humus (Fig. 29). I found no definite buried Altithermal A1 horizon at site 5 BL 120; however, the humus content of unit C-6 suggests that an A horizon was present either *here* or in *close proximity*. Much of the B-horizon oxidation observed in outwash, colluvium, and slopewash underlying the occupation surface is likely to have occurred during this period of warmth and reduced snow cover.

ARRIVAL OF THE ROCK GLACIER

Up to this point in the evolution of the site, we have seen no evidence of a rock glacier at the southern margin of the occupation area. There are no deposits that require its presence; there are no large boulders to indicate that its front towered nearby.

Following occupation, however, the southern margin of the site began to be bombarded with gneissic rockfall boulders. The boulders are larger and more angular than pebbles and cobbles in the underlying outwash; they are identical in size and lithology to boulders in the talus apron at the front of the rock glacier. The lowest angular boulders in the stratigraphic sequence rest directly on occupational charcoal; the highest rest on the modern ground surface, and have rolled to the site in recent years.

Also related to the arrival of the rock glacier is a deposit of dark yellowish brown (10YR 4/4-4/8 m), yellowish brown (10YR 5/6-5/8 m), or strong brown (7.5YR 4/6 m) sand on the inner slope of the moraine (units D-3 and C-7, Figs. 61, 62). Pebbles in the unit are 1 cm or less in maximum dimension. The deposit is structureless, with local areas of subhorizontal bedding. Charcoal and cultural material are absent.

Four characteristics distinguish the deposit from Satanta Peak outwash higher on the moraine: (1) it rests on an erosion surface that transects the Satanta Peak outwash; (2) it contains angular and subangular boulders that have fallen from the rock glacier; (3) it is much finer textured than Satanta Peak outwash; and (4) it contains irregularly-oriented silty inclusions and zones of humus staining.

Two hypotheses of origin were considered. One is that the sand was deposited as outwash from the front of the advancing rock glacier, with concurrent bombardment by rockfall boulders. The second is that the unit is a buried continuation of the "sand ridge" that parallels the rock-glacier front west of the site (pp. 49-53), and is a push moraine or loading feature. If the outwash hypothesis is correct, the hummocky upper surface and steeply-sloping northern face of the deposit must be the result of post-depositional erosion, probably by wind. If the sand-ridge hypothesis is correct, the topography of the deposit may be at least partially constructional.

The absence of deformation in lake sediments beneath the sand (Fig. 62) supports the outwash hypothesis. If, as seems probable, the sand has washed from the front of the rock glacier, it probably did so between 3340 ± 65 BP (I-11,091) and 2970 ± 65 BP (I-11,090), when similar material washed from the rock glacier into the Fourth of July Valley Bog (pp. 60-61).

DEPOSITION OF COLLUVIUM

Units C-8 and D-4 are colluvial in origin, derived from Satanta Peak outwash north and east of the excavation area. Dark yellowish brown (10YR 4/8 m) and strong brown (7.5YR 4/6 m) colors predominate, with darker colors occurring where humus-rich loess has filtered downward from above. Outwash pebbles as large as 6 cm occur in the deposit, which is a stony, gravelly sand or loamy sand, poorly sorted and structureless. Tabular pebbles are aligned with their flat faces parallel to the upper surface of the unit.

The deposit is distinguished from unit C-5 by the preferred orientation of its pebbles and by the stratigraphic superposition apparent in figures 60 and 61. Lake sediments beneath the older colluvial lobe are unoxidized, whereas lake sediments beneath the younger lobe are modified by slopewash and oxidized strong brown (7.5YR 4/6 m), suggesting that deposition of the two colluvial units was separated by an interval of subaerial weathering and erosion.

No artifacts or charcoal were found in colluvium on the lower slope of the moraine, perhaps because of the small volume of material excavated. A short distance to the east, in grid squares 1N/7W, 2N/7W, 1N/8W, and 2N/8W, large quantities of chipping debris were recovered from dark brown (7.5YR 3/4 m) colluvium filling a depression in the outwash surface (Fig. 56 b). The colluvium is thought to correlate with unit C-8.

DEPOSITION OF SLOPEWASH SEDIMENTS

The colluvial deposits just described grade upward into brightly-oxidized (10YR 4/6 to 7.5YR 5/5 m) gravelly sandy clay loam slopewash sediments (units C-9 and D-5). Platy structure and fine vesicularity are characteristic. Pebbles are smaller and less numerous than in underlying colluvium. A high silt-clay content (Fig. 64, sample 4655) suggests a probable loess component. Redeposited charcoal and chipping debris are scattered throughout the deposit; a concentration of lag gravel occurs on its upper surface (Fig. 61).

ORIGIN OF THE CLOSED BASIN

As illustrated in figures 56 b and 56 c, flakes and tools were recovered in large numbers from a closed depression on the lower slope of the moraine. The cultural material was randomly distributed in redeposited loess that filled the depression. There was no indication that the depression had been dug or used by man.

A contour map of the depression (fill re-

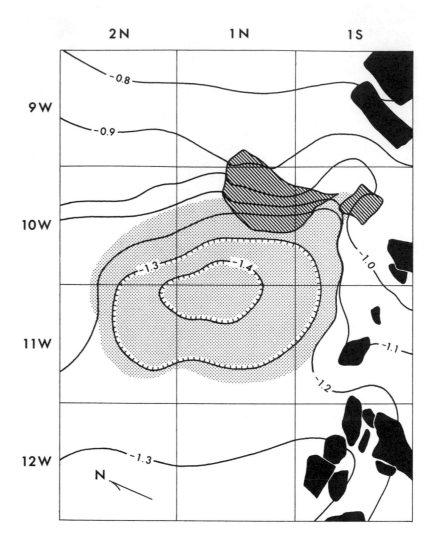

Figure 66. Map of the closed depression on the lower slope of the moraine. Contours are drawn on the surface exposed by removal of artifact-bearing redeposited loess. Elevations are in meters below benchmark A, on the crest of the moraine. Deeply-embedded till boulders are diagonally hatched; boulders that have fallen from the rock glacier are black.

moved) is shown in figure 66. The basin is believed to be of natural origin. The first stage in its development was the formation of an erosion surface and scarp in lake sediments and outwash gravels due to lateral erosion by the North Fork of Middle Boulder Creek; the scarp and its colluvial cover (unit C-5) form the east wall of the basin. The second stage of development occurred when outwash sands (units C-7, D-3) from the front of the rock glacier were deposited, and later scoured by wind, forming the steeply sloping (locally overhanging) south and southwest sides of the basin. The third step was the deposition of colluvial and slopewash units C-8 and C-9, D-4 and D-5, which completed the basin by providing its gravelly northern and northwestern wall.

According to this interpretation, the basin was not yet fully formed at the time of occupation. It developed as the result of a series of geologic coincidences, during a period of perhaps 6000 years, and almost immediately began to fill with fine-textured sediments. I will describe these sediments after discussing the loess that was their source.

LOESS DEPOSITION

The occupation surface is buried by 8 to 16 cm of humus-rich loess (unit A-4). Undisturbed loess occurs only at the crest of the moraine (Figs. 57, 58), where it has a clay loam texture (Fig. 64, samples 4637, 4638), and where a thin, very dark grayish brown (10YR 3/2 m) turf horizon (unit A-5) has developed in its upper few centimeters. The loess becomes lighter-colored with depth, changing from dark brown (10YR 3/3 m), immediately beneath the turf, to dark yellowish brown (10YR 4/4 m), at the base of the unit. Changes in structure and gravel content also occur with depth. Virtually no gravel is present in the upper part of the loess; small quantities appear near its base. The structure of the unit is platy and vesicular throughout; the strength of platiness, however, increases with depth. Vesicles are less than 1 mm in diameter, and occur preferentially along the surfaces of individual platy aggregates.

The loess shows strong vertical jointing, caused by contraction cracks that begin a centimeter or two beneath the turf and extend to the base of the deposit (Figs. 57, 58). Intersecting cracks outline a polygonal pattern with a mesh diameter of 3 to 10 cm, curved sides, and a predominance of right-angle intersections. Patterning is most conspicuous near the base of the loess, where dark-colored, humus-rich soil that has collapsed into the cracks from above contrasts with lighter-colored surrounding soil; closer to the surface, where color differences are absent, the pattern can be discerned only by troweling gently in many directions, dislodging sand grains from the cracks, and leaving the cohesive silty centers of the polygons standing as faintly convex mounds.

I attribute the mudcracks to desiccation, although Cegła (1972) has shown that similar patterns can form by the infiltration of moisture into the pores of dry silt as it accumulates on moist ground; Cegła's experimental patterns appeared as soon as the silt reached a thickness of several millimeters, and remained open throughout deposition.

Chipping debris and charcoal flecks occurred sporadically in unit A-4, but were abundant only near its base. Three chipped-stone tools (Fig. 68 g, h, m) were found in loess on the moraine crest; they are interpreted as having moved upward from the occupation surface due to frost-heaving processes (D. Johnson et al. 1977, Brink 1977). A projectile-point base and midsection (Fig. 67 a) is also believed to have come from unit A-4, although it was not found in situ.

The loess is stratigraphically younger than the earliest influx of boulders from the rock glacier, so is believed to be younger than ca. 3300-3000 ^{14}C yr . Similar loess units occur on the rock-glacier surface (Fig. 39), and at archeological sites 5 BL 170 (Chapter 4) and 5 BL 154 (Fig. 29). At the latter locality the loess rests on charcoal with an age of 3385 ± 95 radiocarbon years (I-11,134).

The thickness of undisturbed loess at site 5 BL 120 (8-16 cm) may give an exaggerated impression of the importance of wind deposition during late- or post-Triple Lakes time. Just as windblown snow becomes concentrated in the dead-air space at the front of the rock glacier, so loess is likely to have been concentrated here by a factor of many times.

FILLING OF THE CLOSED DEPRESSION

The basin shown in figure 66 is filled with dark brown (7.5YR 4/3 m) to dark yellowish brown (10YR 4/4 m) humus-rich clay loam loess. Some of the loess is of direct airfall origin; most, however, appears to have been transported from the occupation area by slopewash. The gravel content of the fill (units C-10, D-6) increases upward from the bottom of the basin, suggesting progressive stripping of a loess mantle from the moraine crest, with exposure of larger and larger areas of subsoil gravel.

The clay-loam texture of the basin fill is intermediate between the texture of undisturbed loess and the texture of underlying outwash and colluvial sediments (Fig. 64, sample 4656). The deposit is finely vesicular, with moderate to strong platy structure. Mudcrack polygons were visible in troweling, but cracks could not be distinguished along profile walls, and are not shown in figures 61 or 62.

Chipping debris and charcoal flecks occurred throughout the basin fill, and chipped-stone tools were recovered from depths of 5 to 48 cm. Included were the bases of four lanceolate projectile points (Fig. 67 d, e, h, k), a finely-serrated projectile-point tip (Fig. 67 r), two smaller point fragments (Fig. 67 o, p), two biface fragments (Fig. 68 a, c), and two edge-retouched flake knives (Fig. 68 e, f). The vertical scatter of chipping debris, charcoal, and artifacts suggests that the basin was never occupied by man; all of the cultural material and most of the loess, together with an admixture of sand and gravel from colluvial and outwash sediments, appear to have been transported from higher on the slope.

The basin is likely to have become filled during Audubon time, when loess was freshly deposited, vegetation on the moraine crest was weakened by late-lying snow, and meltwater for slopewash erosion and redeposition was plentiful. Soil-movement processes are known to have been particularly active at this time (Benedict 1966, 1970), and sediments from the rock-glacier front are thought to have washed into the Fourth of July Valley Bog (p. 61).

Both basins in the southern part of the excavation area continued to fill with sediments until no surface topographic expression remained. The outline of each, however, was indicated by the distribution of Juncus drummondii, a tussock-forming rush that grows preferentially where deep loessal slopewash sediments retain soil moisture (Fig. 56 a). Both basins contained large quantities of redeposited cultural material (Figs. 56 b, 56 c). In retrospect, the correlation between rush-tussock density and artifact distribution was an unusual opportunity for "archeobotanical prospecting".

DEPOSITION OF LOESS-RICH COLLUVIUM

Filling of the basin was followed by an interval of mass wasting, during which colluvial units B-5 and D-7 were deposited on the inner slope of the moraine. The gravelly upper part of unit C-10 is equivalent to these deposits, which are believed to be of Audubon age. The color of the colluvium varies from dark brown (10YR 4/3 m) to strong brown (7.5YR 4/6 m), depending upon its organic-matter content. Sorting is poor; tabular pebbles lie with their flat faces parallel to the sloping ground surface. The silt-clay content of the deposit (Fig. 64, sample 4647) indicates a significant loess component. Charcoal and chipping debris are present. Large angular boulders are embedded in the unit near the front of the rock glacier.

SLOPEWASH AND MASS-WASTING

The youngest deposit at the site (units B-6, C-11, D-8) is a mixture of reworked loess and outwash. It occurs in eroded areas on the inner slope of the moraine, where meltwater from the late-lying snowbank encourages slow downslope soil movement under the influence of needle-ice, frost-creep, and slopewash processes. Sediments forming the deposit are supplied by continuing headward erosion into well-vegetated loess and turf on the moraine crest. The unit contains considerable organic matter, and has a gravelly sandy clay loam texture (Figs. 63-64, samples 4646, 4649). Its structure is weakly blocky to platy; fine vesicles are present. Colors vary from dark gray (10YR 4/1 m) to very dark grayish brown (10YR 4/2 m) or brown (10YR 4/3-5/3 m).

Six projectile-point fragments (Fig. 67 *c*, *g*, *i*, *j*, *m*, *n*), and seven chipped-stone tools (Fig. 68 *b*, *d*, *i*, *j*, *k*, *l*, *o*) were collected from the lag-gravel surface of the deposit. Beneath the gravel, at depths of 1½ to 2 cm in slopewash and mass-wasting debris, a stemmed projectile point (Fig. 67 *l*), the bases of two lanceolate points (Fig. 67 *b*, *f*), and a projectile-point tip (Fig. 67 *q*) were recovered. Chipping debris and charcoal occurred throughout the deposit; a lack of oxidation beneath the charcoal suggests redeposition from higher on the slope.

Artifacts

Cultural material from the site consisted of 18 projectile points and point fragments, 2 bifacial cutting tools, 2 biface fragments of unknown function, 3 edge-retouched flakes, a utilized prismatic flake, a chopper/scraper, the nucleus of a chalcedony core, 5 perforating tools, and 1392 flakes. No grinding implements were recovered. All of the chipped-stone tools are consistent with hunting and butchering activities; they suggest that a small party of hunters camped briefly on the moraine crest to replace broken projectile points and to process meat, hides, and bone.

The distribution of cultural material found during excavation is shown in figures 56 b and 56 c. Flakes and artifacts from the surface are not plotted, due to inadequate provenience data.

PROJECTILE POINTS

Lanceolate Points (11 specimens, Fig. 67 *a-k*).

Tip. No data.

Blade. Symmetrically lanceolate, widest 2-3 cm above the base. Three fragments (Fig. 67 *a*, *b*, *j*) show fine parallel-oblique flaking on one or both faces; flake scars cross the blade from upper left to lower right at angles of 60°-75° with its long axis. Flaking on a fourth point fragment (Fig. 67 *g*) is irregularly parallel-transverse on both faces.

Shoulders. None.

Hafting Area. Heavily ground for distances of 11-22 mm forward from the base.

Stem. None.

Base. Concave to very concave. Thinned by striking 1 to 3 shallow longitudinal flakes from each side of a basal platform prepared by heavy grinding. Basal concavities are 2-5 mm deep, and are unground or only lightly ground.

Cross-Section. Bi-convex in transverse and longitudinal section.

Dimensions. The points are estimated to have originally been longer than 70 mm. They are 18-25 mm wide and 4.6-6.9 mm thick.

Rock Types. Fine-grained white to gray quartzite (10); fine-grained pinkish brown quartzite (1). Experiments show that yellow- and buff-tinged varieties of the gray quartzite oxidize pinkish brown when heated. A single quartzite source can account for all projectile points from the site.

Provenience. *a*, found in 1975 while reopening the east wall of grid square 2S/1W to sample the upper loess unit for possible ^{14}C dating. Depth is uncertain; the point is oxidized by burning, and was probably associated with charcoal in stratigraphic unit A-4. *b*, 1S/12W, 2-cm depth. *c*, surface gravel, west of excavation area. *d*, 1S/10W, 14-cm depth. *e*, 1N/10W, 48-cm depth. *f*, 1N/6W, 2-cm depth. *g*, surface gravel, collected by Husted (1965, Fig. 1 *e*). *h*, 1N/10W, 22-cm depth. *i*, surface gravel, west of excavation area. *j*, surface gravel, collected by Husted (1965, Fig. 1 *a*). *k*, 1N/11W, 46-cm depth.

Wear Patterns. Blade edges show light to moderate rounding, blunting, and step flaking[16]. Broken edges are unworn except for a burin-like lateral fracture on the left side of the point in figure 67 *g*. Surface wear is limited to slight rounding of flake ridges. One of the points (Fig. 67 *b*) shows faint alternate edge retouch; the right edge of each face (tip up) is steeper than the left edge.

Remarks. The lower blade edge of one of the points (Fig. 67 *k*, left side) is a steep, flat fracture, broken during manufacture or during an early episode of use. The broken edge was ground for hafting.

Stemmed Points (2 specimens, Fig. 67 *l-m*).

Tip. Originally sharp; blunted by use.

Blade. Symmetrically ovate, narrowing from shoulders to tip. Fully flaked on both faces. One face of the complete point is flaked obliquely from upper left to lower right, with parallel flake scars that meet the long axis of the point at an angle of 45°; flaking on the other face (illustrated in Fig. 67 *l*) is collateral, with the suggestion of a faint medial ridge.

[16] *Edge-wear terminology follows Ahler (1971).*

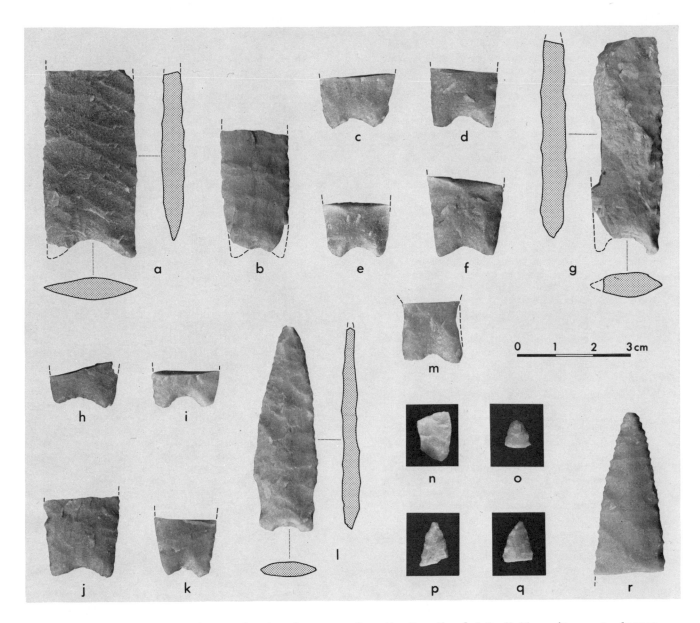

Figure 67. Projectile points and point fragments from the Fourth of July Valley site. *a-k*, lanceolate points; *l-m*, stemmed points; *n-r*, unclassifiable fragments.

Shoulders. Gently sloping.

Hafting Area. Heavily ground.

Stem. Very slightly expanding, accounting for about one-quarter of the total length of the complete point.

Base. Shallowly notched. The basal notch is 1½ to 2 mm deep and 6 to 7 mm wide. Heavy grinding extends to the edges of the notch; the notch itself is unground or lightly ground.

Cross-Section. Bi-convex in transverse section. The unbroken point is made on a slightly curved flake, thickest near the junction of stem and blade.

Dimensions. Length 54 mm, width 17 mm, haft-ing width 14 mm, thickness 4.8 mm.

Rock Types. Fine-grained gray quartzite (2).

Provenience. *l*, 1S/9W, 2-cm depth. *m*, surface gravel, collected by Husted (1965, Fig. 1 *b*).

Wear Patterns. The blade edges and tip of the unbroken point are rounded, blunted, and step flaked. Rounding and smoothing of flake ridges and other projections on the surface of the blade suggest deep penetration into soft material. Steep tiny retouch flake scars on the right side of each face indicate that blade edges were sharpened (or serrated) prior to most recent use.

Unclassifiable Point Fragments (5 specimens, Fig. 67 n-r). The hafting area and basal concavity of the gray quartzite projectile-point base fragment shown in figure 67 n are heavily ground. Four projectile point tips, also of gray quartzite, are sharp to very sharp; only the smallest shows evidence of wear.

A large tip/midsection fragment (Fig. 67 r) exhibits well-executed parallel-oblique flaking on both faces. Flake scars intersect the long axis of the blade at an angle of 60°, trending from upper left to lower right; flaking changes to transverse near the tip. Blade edges are delicately serrated, with 5 to 6 serrations per centimeter. Serration was accomplished by detaching small pressure flakes unifacially from one edge of the blade, then rotating the point on its axis and repeating the process on the other edge. Use wear is minimal; if the tool had been used more heavily, its serrations would have been worn away, and its blade edges would resemble the alternately-beveled edges of several other projectile points from the site.

Provenience: n, surface gravel (Husted flake collection. o, 1N/11W, 14-cm depth. p, 1N/11W, depth uncertain. q, 1N/10W, 1½-cm depth. r, 1N/10W, 38-cm depth.

CHIPPED-STONE TOOLS

Biface Fragment (Fig. 68 a). A gray quartzite biface, probably a cutting tool, was recovered from 5- to 6-cm depth in grid square 1N/11W. Flaking is unpatterned, and not as well executed as on projectile points from the site. Working edge angles range from 35° to 55°; rounding, blunting, and light step flaking are evidence of use.

Biface Fragment (Fig. 68 b). The tip of a second quartzite biface was collected by Husted from the lag-gravel surface. Its blade is broad (27 mm at the fracture) and thin (4.7 mm); working edge angles of 30°-45° suggest a cutting function. Rounding, blunting, and step flaking are the principal forms of edge wear. One face of the blade was flaked obliquely (upper right to lower left) at an angle of 60° with the longitudinal; flake scars on the other face trend at right angles to blade edges.

Biface Fragments (Fig. 68 c-d). Two biface fragments are illustrated in figure 68 c-d. Each is the striking-platform end of a bifacially-flaked implement of unknown function. The tools were used intensively. Their working edges show rounding, crushing, and step flaking; hinge fractures are unworn, as are the pointed intersections of broken and worked edges. Both tool fragments are made of gray quartzite. The smaller fragment is from the Husted flake collection; the larger is from redeposited loess in grid square 1N/10W.

Edge-Retouched Flake Knife (Fig. 68 e). A knife made by retouching the edges of an otherwise-unmodified flat, oval flake of gray and white chert was found at 48-cm depth in grid square 1N/11W. Edge retouch is bifacial and discontinuous. Working edge angles of 20° to 35° suggest a cutting function; step flaking is the principal form of edge wear.

Edge-Retouched Flake Knife (Fig. 68 f). A small flake knife made of brecciated tan, brown, and pink chert was found at 4- to 5-cm depth in grid square 1N/10W. The chert is distinctive because of its pink stylolitic sutures and subtle range of colors; its source outcrop is unknown. The flake appears to have been struck from the edge of a large, utilized biface, and is thin and oval, with sharp natural edges (15°-35°), suitable for cutting. Fine edge retouch, probably intentional, occurs around the entire periphery of the flake except for the striking platform, alternating between the dorsal and ventral surfaces of the flake. Slight blunting is the principal form of edge wear.

Utilized Prismatic Blade (Fig. 68 g). Two pieces of a utilized prismatic blade were found in grid square 3S/2W, adjacent to the shallow-basin hearth; the smallest fragment lay on the gravel surface, and the largest in loess at a depth of 5-7 cm. The tool is made of fossiliferous brown chert, containing black dendritic inclusions. A striking platform is preserved at the narrow end of the blade. All lateral edges are utilized, with rounding and nibbling the principal forms of edge wear; rounding and polish occur locally at the junctions between flake scars on the dorsal surface of the tool. Expanding flake scars with steep to overhanging hinged terminations may record purposeful retouch of lateral edges prior to use. Edge angles of 35°-90° would have been suitable for a variety of functions.

Chopper or Scraper (Fig. 68 h). A large chopping or scraping tool was found in undisturbed loess at 3- to 5-cm depth in grid square 2N/1W, on the crest of the moraine. The tool is made from a thick, wedge-shaped flake of gray quartzite; an irregular striking platform forms the blunt edge of the wedge. Retouch is limited to steep unifacial pressure flaking along the evenly arcuate transverse distal margin of the tool; edge angles vary from 55° to 75°. Edge wear is discontinuous, suggesting partial resharpening before the tool was discarded.

Edge-Retouched Flake (Fig. 68 i). An irregularly-shaped flake of fossiliferous, dendritic brown chert, found on the gravel surface, has been intensively utilized. The flake consists of two connected lobes, separated by a V-shaped reentrant. One lobe is rounded and one pointed; each has a medial ridge and triangular cross-section. Both lobes were retouched unifacially (dorsal side only) by the removal of tiny flakes from their edges. Rounding, the principal form of edge wear on both lobes, is absent in the reentrant between them. Reflective areas on flake surfaces appear to be a characteristic of the chert rather than the result of use polish.

Flake Perforators (Fig. 68 j-k). Two small

Figure 68.   Chipped-stone tools and waste flakes from the Fourth of July Valley site. *a–d*, biface fragments; *e–f*, *i*, edge-retouched flakes; *g*, utilized prismatic blade; *h*, chopper or scraper; *j–k*, flake perforators; *l*, flake with chisel bit; *m*, core nucleus; *n–o*, flake gravers; *p–q*, large, non-utilized flakes. S.P. = striking platform.

flake perforators found on the ground surface are made from expanding flakes of fossiliferous, dendritic brown chert. Each perforating bit is formed by the distal end and a lateral edge of the flake. These meet at an acute angle, forming a natural point that has been accentuated by fine marginal retouch, primarily unifacial. The tips of the perforators are blunted by use.

Tool with Chisel Bit (Fig. 68 *l*). Another example of a flake converted to a tool by minimal modification was found by Husted in gravel on the inner slope of the moraine. The tool is made from a thick, chunky fragment of fossiliferous brown chert, with sharply angular edges resulting from the tendency of this rock type to fracture irregularly. The narrow end of the tool was notched by unifacial pressure flaking to accentuate its chisel bit. The natural edge angle of the bit is 40°; fine unifacial pressure retouch has steepened this angle to about 60°. Blunting is the only important form of edge wear on the bit.

Core (Fig. 68 *m*). A core of milky white chalcedony, roughly equidimensional, was found in undisturbed loess on the moraine crest (grid square 2N/2E), at 5- to 6-cm depth. Flakes have been struck from all sides of the core; there is no evidence of a prepared platform. The core was discarded without use. Flakes of this rock type are absent at the site, and it is unlikely that tools were manufactured from it on the moraine.

Flake Gravers (Fig. 68 *n-o*). Two small flake gravers were recovered from the site. The first (Fig. 68 *n*), made of fine-grained gray quartzite, was found in grid square 1N/7W; its depth and stratigraphic associations are uncertain. The tool was shaped by alternately removing a single shallow flake from the left side (tip down) of each face of the graving tip. The tip is rounded by heavy use.

The second graver (Fig. 68 *o*) was found on the ground surface. It is made of a flake of pink chalcedony, finely flecked with red. The graving tip was formed by steep unifacial (dorsal side only) edge retouch. Rounding and fine step flaking are evidence of use.

Large, Unmodified Flakes (Fig. 68 *p-q*). Several large quartzite flakes with sharp (15°-40°) natural edges were discarded at the site. Given the effectiveness of such flakes for certain cutting operations (Walker 1978) and the absence of local sources of workable stone, the lack of wear along their edges is surprising.

CHIPPING DEBRIS

Waste flakes from excavations at the site numbered 1210; an additional 182 flakes were collected from the surface during our own and Husted's site surveys. Most of the flakes were small, averaging about a centimeter in length (Fig. 69). They occurred in all

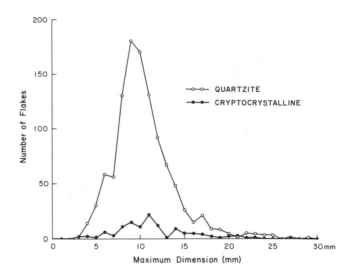

Figure 69. Dimensions of excavated flakes from the Fourth of July Valley site. Flakes smaller than 8-9 mm are underrepresented due to the use of ¼-inch mesh in screening.

stratigraphic units above the occupation surface, except for the modern turf horizon and outwash from the rock glacier, but were most numerous in depressions on the lower slope of the moraine (Fig. 56 b).

Functional analysis of the chipping debris provided no conclusive evidence for tool manufacture. Of the 434 flakes whose striking platforms were preserved, only 10.4% lacked evidence of wear. The scarcity of cores and absence of decortication flakes suggest that tool manufacture, *if* it occurred at the site, was limited to final shaping of preforms imported from other localities, or to the reworking of broken implements.

Resharpening of use-dulled tools was a much more important activity. Remnants of former working edges, rounded, blunted, or otherwise modified by use, suggest that at least 89.6% of the flakes with striking platforms were detached during tool resharpening. Two varieties of quartzite and nine cryptocrystalline rock types are represented, implying that eleven or more tools were resharpened. Working edge angles cluster between 55° and 85° (Fig. 70); the tools from which these flakes were detached might have been useful for hide scraping (Hayden 1979) or woodworking (T. Miller 1979), two activities that are otherwise poorly documented at the site.

Attempts to delimit work areas on the basis of flake types were productive only on the moraine crest; concentrations of flakes on the inner slope of the moraine (Figs. 71 a, b) mark the locations of natural sediment traps, rather than human activities. Both fireplaces on the moraine crest were centers for tool repair (Fig. 71 b); quartzite tools were resharpened near the open fireplace in grid square 1S/1W (Fig. 71 c), and chert and chalcedony tools were resharpened at the periphery of the basin hearth in grid square 2S/2W (Fig.

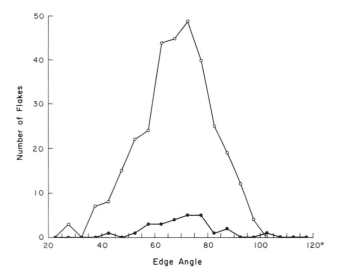

Figure 70. Edge angles of excavated resharpening flakes. A contact goniometer was used to measure the angle between (a) a tangent to the striking platform of the flake and (b) a tangent to its dorsal surface immediately behind the zone of wear. This angle is believed to approximate the working edge angle of the tool that was resharpened.

71 d). A concentration of burned quartzite and chert flakes in the vicinity of grid squares 1S/4W and 1S/5W (Figs. 71 c, d) indicates that a hearth may formerly have been present nearby; however, no charcoal or scorched earth were found in the vicinity.

Rock Types

A scant 15 rock types were present in the flake collection, consistent with a single visit by a group whose tool kit contained a limited number of lithic materials. Of 1210 excavated flakes, 89.9% were quartzite and 10.1% were chert or chalcedony. Silicified wood was absent. Descriptions of the principal rock types are in Appendix A.

Comparison of rock types used in tool manufacture with samples from nearby quarry sites suggests possible sources for three of the most abundant lithic materials. The commonest rock type, a very fine-grained white to gray or buff orthoquartzite with widely-scattered heavy-mineral inclusions, is identical to material from the Spanish Diggings of eastern Wyoming (Saul 1964), where it occurs in altered sandstones of the Cloverly Formation (Cretaceous). Sources closer to the Front Range may exist, but I have not yet found them.

A brown, dendritic, fossiliferous chert, used in the manufacture of five tools, is al-

so similar to material from the Spanish Diggings area, although it has not been *precisely* duplicated in outcrop. Identifiable fossils are of Pennsylvanian age (John Chronic, pers. comm. 1980); they include a fusilinid, a biserial foraminifer (cf. *Textularia*), and a bryozoan (*Rhombopora* sp.).

The knife in figure 68 e is made of gray to white chalcedony containing diffuse spherical inclusions of opaque white chert. Similar material has been collected at localities in Middle and North Parks. Its closest known occurrence is in the Troublesome Formation (Tertiary), near Kremmling, Colorado.

Functional Interpretation of the Projectile Points

HAFTING-ELEMENT DESIGN

Obliquely-flaked stemmed and lanceolate projectile points occur together at sites in Utah (Jennings 1957), central Texas (Alexander 1963), Kansas (Katz 1971, 1973), and northern Wyoming (Frison 1973). At each of these localities the points were found in pre-Altithermal components that contained evidence of seed gathering and plant-food preparation. Several of the excavators noted a similarity in artifact classes and subsistence activities to those of the McKean complex (Mulloy 1954), a post-Altithermal cultural assemblage in which stemmed and lanceolate projectile points also occur together.

Four possible explanations exist for the co-occurrence of two hafting-element designs at the Fourth of July Valley site:

(1) Two components may be represented, each characterized by a different projectile-point style. This hypothesis is rejected because lanceolate and stemmed points from the site are made of identical light gray quartzite, and involve identical flaking technologies, wear patterns, and resharpening techniques.

(2) Different functions may have been involved. Aikens (1970: 189), for example, has suggested that crudely-executed stemmed points from the early levels of Hogup Cave were used as dart points for hunting pronghorn and deer, whereas well-made, obliquely-flaked lanceolate points were used with thrusting spears for hunting bison and mountain sheep. Such functional differences cannot be excluded at the Fourth of July Valley site, although the likelihood that more than a single species of large game animal was hunted during the brief period of occupation is considered slight. The possibility that differences in hafting-element design were related to differences in secondary (butchering) function is rejected, because both point styles have similar edge angles (30°-55°) and similar

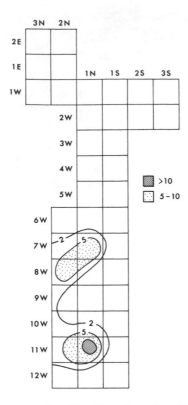

a. Possible Manufacturing Flakes
(flakes per m²)

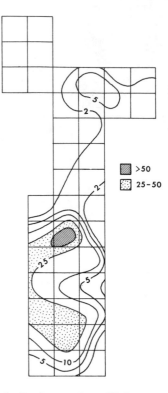

b. Resharpening Flakes
(flakes per m²)

Figure 71. Distribution of chipping debris in the excavation area.

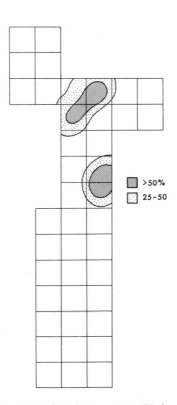

c. Oxidized Quartzite Flakes
(percent of total quartzite)

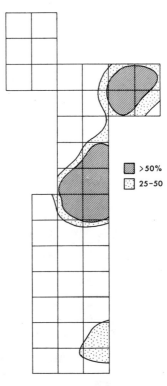

d. Cryptocrystalline Flakes
(percent of total flakes)

kinds of edge wear (rounding, blunting, step flaking).

(3) Stems may have been added to lanceolate points so that the points could be hafted to foreshafts with smaller diameters than those for which they were originally designed. This might have become necessary if foreshafts were broken or lost in the timberline environment, where replacement materials were scarce and undersized. The range of hafting widths for lanceolate points from the site is 17-24 mm; the range for stemmed points is 14-15 mm.

(4) Stems may have been added to broken projectile-point tips to facilitate rehafting. The abundance of discarded projectile-point bases at the site shows that replacement of broken weapon points *was* an important activity; recycling of large tip and blade fragments is suggested by the underrepresentation of these elements in the collection.

ALTERNATE EDGE BEVELING

Alternate edge beveling is regarded by many as a product of biface resharpening (Sollberger 1971); less commonly it is viewed as a means of rejuvenating broken projectile points (Frison and Grey 1980). At the Fourth of July Valley site, micro-beveling of projectile-point edges seems to have had a *third* explanation: serration for a specialized cutting function, followed by attrition during use. As seen in figure 67 *r*, serration was applied unifacially to one blade edge; the point was then rotated on its axis and the process repeated on the other side. Use as a cutting tool destroyed the serrations, but failed to obliterate the unifacial retouch scars between them.

A serrated blade edge is useful for sawing and slicing soft material, as in hide stripping, meat carving, shredding of vegetation, and fish scaling (Ahler 1971, J. Nance 1971). Considering the resources available in the Fourth of July valley, the points are most likely to have been used as skinning knives and/or for cutting meat. Surface wear suggests deep penetration into relatively soft material, and step flaking indicates that working edges came into occasional contact with hard substances such as bone. All points and point fragments larger than 3 cm show evidence of secondary use as cutting tools.

The Paleo Indian - McKean Transition

Two problems in Plains archeology, first recognized several decades ago, have stubbornly resisted solution. One is the disappearance of late Paleo-Indian cultural complexes from the Northwestern Plains at the beginning of the Altithermal; the other is the origin of the McKean complex, which appeared in the same region about 2500 radiocarbon years later.

"There are no local cultural continuities from Paleo Indian to Post-Altithermal that can be satisfactorily traced from the stratigraphic record ... McKean and its variants cannot be given clear-cut antecedents on the basis of projectile point typology" (Frison 1973: 310).

Both problems may eventually prove to have a single solution, rooted in climatic change and in the nature of the Plains environment. In a preliminary discussion of the Fourth of July Valley site, Benedict and Olson (1973) hypothesized that the McKean complex developed from a Paleo-Indian cultural base in Altithermal refugia, and that at least part of this development occurred in high-altitude refuge areas such as the Colorado Front Range. The concept of such a developmental sequence was not new. D.C. Grey (pers. comm. to Husted 1969: 86) had earlier suggested that the Pryor Stemmed projectile point, used between 8500 and 7500 yr BP in the foothills of Wyoming and Montana, was ancestral to the stemmed, indented-base "Duncan" point of the McKean complex. A difficulty with Grey's hypothesis, and with a more elaborate hypothesis developed by Husted (1968, 1969), was the 2500-yr time gap for which no information was available. Husted's (1974) attempt to bridge the gap with a cultural complex excavated by Sanger (1963, 1966, 1967) in the Lochnore-Nesikep area of southern British Columbia was particularly unconvincing. The Fourth of July Valley site is a more satisfactory bridge between late Paleo Indian and McKean, demonstrating the existence of a typologically- and chronologically-intermediate stage in what appears to have been a developmental continuum.

TYPOLOGICAL COMPARISONS

The hypothesis of cultural continuity relies heavily on the argument that certain projectile-point styles used on the Northwestern Plains immediately prior to the Altithermal were ancestral to those used in the same region after the return to cooler, moister, post-Altithermal conditions. The critical Paleo-Indian point styles are obliquely-flaked forms such as James Allen[17] and Pryor Stemmed points. The critical Middle Plains Archaic styles are those of the McKean complex, particularly McKean Lanceolate and Duncan points (Fig. 72). Descriptions of these four point styles are in Appendix B. The principal stylistic changes occurring during the Altithermal were the following:

----

[17] *James Allen (Mulloy 1959: 114), Lusk (Irwin-Williams et al. 1973: 51), Frederick (Irwin-Williams et al. 1973: 50), and Angostura (Agogino et al. 1964: 1351-52) points are considered here to be related variants.*

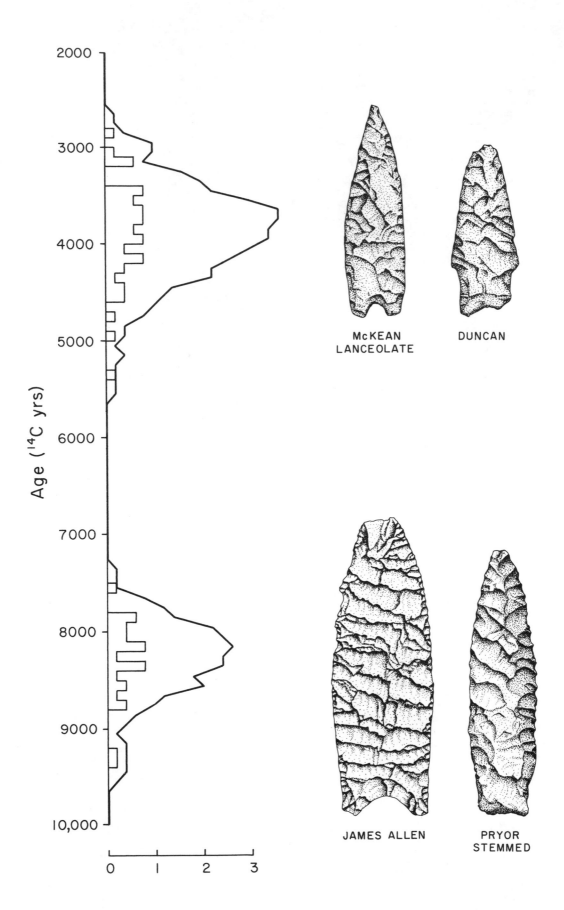

McKEAN
LANCEOLATE

DUNCAN

JAMES ALLEN

PRYOR
STEMMED

Age (^{14}C yrs)

2000

3000

4000

5000

6000

7000

8000

9000

10,000

0   1   2   3

(1) For the transition from James Allen to McKean Lanceolate points: (a) a reduction in size; (b) a change from good-quality bifacial parallel-oblique pressure flaking to poorer-quality random or collateral flaking, some-times incomplete on one face of the point; (c) an increased incidence of edge beveling and serration — cf. the Dead Indian Creek site (Frison 1978, Fig. 2.9) and the McKean level of Mummy Cave (Husted 1978: 62); (d) the virtual disappearance of grinding from basal concavities and lower blade edges; and (e) a trend toward proportionally deeper, nar-rower basal notches.

(2) For the proposed transition from Pryor Stemmed to Duncan projectile points: (a) a re-duction in length, producing a proportionally broader point; (b) a change from parallel-oblique to random flaking, sometimes incom-plete; (c) a reduced incidence of edge bevel-ing and serration; and (d) a decline in the importance of basal grinding.

Projectile points from the Fourth of July Valley site are intermediate in size, form, and technique of manufacture. Parallel-oblique and random flaking are both repre-sented. Stems and lower blade edges are heav-ily ground, but basal notches are unground or very lightly ground. Alternate edge retouch occurs on lanceolate as well as on stemmed forms, but is not nearly as well developed as on Pryor Stemmed points, perhaps because of the thinness of the Fourth of July valley specimens.

CHRONOLOGICAL COMPARISONS

A second requirement of the hypothesis is that the Fourth of July Valley site be intermediate in age. Figure 72 is a summary, by radiocarbon century, of published dates for parallel-oblique-flaked stemmed and lan-ceolate projectile points and for McKean Lan-ceolate and Duncan points in the Northwest Plains culture area. Solid-carbon dates and dates determined in private laboratories are excluded, as are dates for bone carbonate and apatite. Site locations and references are in figure 73.

Figure 72 (facing page). Radiocarbon dates for archeological components with obliquely-flaked late Paleo-Indian and McKean projec-tile-point styles, western plains and moun-tains. Site locations are in figure 73. The heavy line is a 500-yr running mean showing dates per radiocarbon century (scale at bot-tom). Projectile points are from the Mule Creek, Bottleneck Cave, and James Allen sites, and are redrawn natural size from We-del (1961), Husted (1969), and Frison (1978). They are believed to represent end members in a developmental continuum that spanned the Altithermal; typologically-intermediate forms are present at the Fourth of July Val-ley site.

The Fourth of July Valley site, dated at about 5960 ± 85 radiocarbon yr BP, is 1500 years younger than the youngest obliquely-flaked Paleo-Indian projectile points yet found in a dated context on the Northwestern Plains, and 1000 years older than the earliest Plains occurrences of McKean Lanceolate and Duncan point styles[18]. Both of the Fourth of July val-ley dates are for large samples of wood char-coal, free of rootlets and adhering loess. The charcoal was collected in clear association with cultural material in a single-component occupation site. The dates provide strong sup-port for the hypothesis of cultural continuity.

EVALUATION

Lanceolate projectile points from the Fourth of July Valley site closely resemble James Allen and related forms; I interpret them as Altithermal holdovers of these late Paleo-Indian styles, and as probable ancestors to the McKean Lanceolate point. Stemmed points from the site resemble Pryor Stemmed and Dun-can points, but are not necessarily related to them: stemming may have been primarily a means of recycling broken projectile-point tips, or of adapting lanceolate points to small-diameter replacement foreshafts; alternate edge beveling may have had no special significance other than that serrated blade edges were needed for a specialized cutting operation (pp. 85-87).

No substantive changes in economy were re-quired by the transition from terminal Paleo Indian to McKean. A wide range of ecological niches was exploited by both groups during the course of a carefully-scheduled seasonal round such as is hypothesized for the occupants of the Fourth of July Valley site. Differences in climate may have caused greater emphasis on foothills and mountain environments prior to 7500 BP, and greater utilization of the open High Plains following 5000 BP (compare figures 73 a and 73 b).

It is uncertain whether *all*, or only *part*, of the transition from Paleo Indian to McKean occurred in the high mountains. The Front Range is likely to have been unsuitable for occupa-tion during part of this time period (Benedict 1979a), as for example during the Ptarmigan advance (Chapter 2). Obliquely-flaked lanceolate projectile points occur at all altitudes in the Front Range, from the foothills[19] to the high-est tundra ridges. A great deal of typological variation is represented, suggesting consider-able time depth. It may eventually prove that the Southern Rocky Mountains were occupied con-tinuously during the Altithermal interval, but that centers of population density shifted be-tween areas east and west of the continental divide in response to changes in the distribu-tion of winter snowfall related to changes in the zonality of atmospheric circulation.

---

[18] *The date of 5300 BP shown in figure 72 is for a McKean component at the Hungry Whistler site, above timberline in the Front Range.*

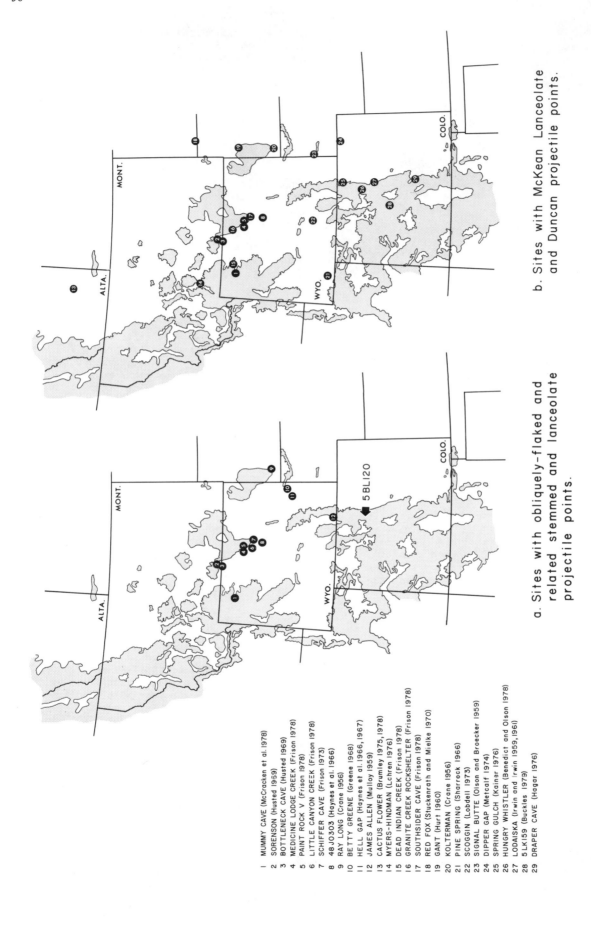

1 MUMMY CAVE (McCracken et al.1978)
2 SORENSON (Husted 1969)
3 BOTTLENECK CAVE (Husted 1969)
4 MEDICINE LODGE CREEK (Frison 1978)
5 PAINT ROCK V (Frison 1978)
6 LITTLE CANYON CREEK (Frison 1978)
7 SCHIFFER CAVE (Frison 1973)
8 48JO3O3 (Haynes et al. 1966)
9 RAY LONG (Crane 1956)
10 BETTY GREENE (Greene 1968)
11 HELL GAP (Haynes et al.1966, 1967)
12 JAMES ALLEN (Mulloy 1959)
13 CACTUS FLOWER (Brumley 1975,1978)
14 MYERS-HINDMAN (Lahren 1976)
15 DEAD INDIAN CREEK (Frison 1978)
16 GRANITE CREEK ROCKSHELTER (Frison 1978)
17 SOUTHSIDER CAVE (Frison 1978)
18 RED FOX (Stuckenrath and Mielke 1970)
19 GANT (Hurt 1960)
20 KOLTERMAN (Crane 1956)
21 PINE SPRING (Sharrock 1966)
22 SCOGGIN (Lobdell 1973)
23 SIGNAL BUTTE (Olson and Broecker 1959)
24 DIPPER GAP (Metcalf 1974)
25 SPRING GULCH (Kainer 1976)
26 HUNGRY WHISTLER (Benedict and Olson 1978)
27 LODAISKA (Irwin and Irwin 1959,1961)
28 5LKI59 (Buckles 1979)
29 DRAPER CAVE (Hagar 1976)

a. Sites with obliquely-flaked and
   related stemmed and lanceolate
   projectile points.

b. Sites with McKean Lanceolate
   and Duncan projectile points.

Figure 73. Locations of dated sites used in constructing the histograms in figure 72. Forested uplands are shaded.

The sequence described above is viewed as a local (Colorado-Wyoming) manifestation of a much more widespread phenomenon, occurring in many different Altithermal refugia and involving a diversity of Paleo-Indian projectile-point styles (James Allen, Humboldt Concave-base, Plainview *golondrina*, etc.) that share a common flavor, although not precise identity.

A problem that will not be discussed here, but that may be related in some way to the Altithermal refugium concept, is the late persistence of parallel-oblique-flaked projectile points along the Arctic coast of Alaska, at sites such as Cape Krusenstern (Giddings 1963) and Iyatayet (Giddings 1964). These late northern occurrences are of interest because, like obliquely-flaked points from the Fourth of July Valley site, they indicate the late survival of a Paleo-Indian flaking technology in a moist, low-temperature environment.

Summary

GEOLOGIC HISTORY

The oldest deposits at the Fourth of July Valley site are till, lake sediments, and outwash; they document a shift from glacial to lacustrine to glaciofluvial sedimentation during the multiple ice advances of Satanta Peak time. Slump structures in the outwash show that ice persisted in the core of the moraine until the close of the second Satanta Peak advance; the intervening non-glacial interval cannot have been warm enough, or long-lasting enough, for total melting to occur. A radiocarbon date for organic carbon in the proglacial lake silts is rejected because of probable contamination by rootlets enriched in fallout radionuclides; dates from a nearby bog show that Satanta Peak deposits at the site are older than 9215 ± 105 BP.

An erosion surface and scarp were cut in sediments on the inner slope of the moraine when the North Fork of Middle Boulder Creek swung eastward into the excavation area as it meandered on its high floodplain. The scarp is mantled with colluvium. Because the colluvium

[19] *An interesting foothills occurrence is at the Magic Mountain site, west of Denver, where two obliquely-flaked lanceolate points were associated with Scottsbluff-Eden points, a Cody knife, and an Agate Basin point in a context (Zone D) that was believed to be much too recent. The points were attributed to aboriginal collecting, because "to give greater significance to them would infer a very late survival in the area of these complexes" (Irwin-Williams and Irwin 1966: 85).*

contains no loess, it must be older than 8270 ± 140 radiocarbon years, the minimum age of loess at a nearby locality on Satanta Peak outwash.

Two loess units are present on the moraine crest. The oldest, which has been extensively reworked by frost action and slopewash processes, was deposited prior to 5960 ± 85 radiocarbon years BP, the average age of charcoal in fireplaces on its surface. Graveliness, bright oxidation, and moderate to low organic-matter content distinguish the deposit from a younger loess unit that overlies the occupation surface. The latter is less gravelly, darker brown in color, and richer in organic matter; it was deposited during post-Triple Lakes time.

A rock glacier at the southern margin of the site belongs to the younger of two generations of lobate rock glaciers that occur in the study area, and elsewhere in the Indian Peaks. The stratigraphic positions of angular boulders that have fallen from the rock glacier into the excavation area, and of a coarse sand unit believed to have washed from its front, indicate that the feature advanced to the margin of the site after 5960 ± 85 BP and prior to deposition of the younger loess. Additional evidence for the age of the rock glacier is discussed on pp. 48-49.

Artifacts were extensively redistributed by mass-wasting and slopewash processes following deposition of the younger loess. They accumulated in natural sediment traps on the lower slopes of the moraine, primarily during Audubon time.

CULTURAL HISTORY

The site was visited briefly, in late summer or fall, by a single band of transient hunters. Chipped-stone tools are consistent with butchering, hide preparation, and working of wood or bone; at least eleven implements, most of them scrapers or woodworking tools, were resharpened on the moraine. Projectile points were used secondarily as hafted knives, and several were serrated for specialized skinning and/or meat-cutting operations. A broken projectile point was burinated. I do not know what species of animals were hunted, or whether game-drive hunting techniques were employed. The campsite is small, and by itself would probably not have accommodated the number of people required to operate a large-scale communal drive. However, the abundance of broken projectile-point bases on the moraine may indicate a kill of proportions that would have required game-drive hunting, rather than stalking of individual animals; activities at the site may have spilled over onto nearby outwash terraces, allowing a relatively large group to make use of the area.

I found no evidence of gathering or grinding at the site, although the cultural relationships of its inhabitants lie with groups that are known to have made intensive use of plant foods in other environments. Projectile points broken during the hunt were replaced on the moraine crest, either with new points manufac-

92

tured elsewhere, or with broken specimens modified for re-use. There is no conclusive evidence *for* or *against* tool manufacture at the
site. The principal rock types in the tool
and flake collection are an even-grained,
light gray orthoquartzite and a dendritic,
fossiliferous brown chert, both of which
could have been quarried in the Spanish Diggings area, 300 km to the north-northeast[20].

The plains and the high mountains, separated by only a few tens of kilometers, represent opposite environmental extremes. Each is
a "good times-bad times" environment, in which
human occupation is unlikely to have been continuous for long periods of time. Drought is a
principal limiting factor on the plains, and
snowfall a principal limiting factor in the
mountains. Occupation of the Fourth of July
Valley site, 5960 ± 85 radiocarbon years ago,
coincided with one of the most severe droughts
of postglacial time — an interval during which
cultural groups from many parts of the arid
west converged upon the Indian Peaks region
(Benedict 1979*a*). Obliquely-flaked stemmed and
lanceolate projectile points indicate the persistence of an important late Paleo-Indian
complex at the moist western periphery of the
plains long after its disappearance from the
drier, shortgrass environment. The age of the
site, and the size, form, and technology of
its projectile points, suggest that a developmental stage in the evolution of the McKean
complex may be represented. Excavation and
dating of other high-altitude and foothills
sites with transitional projectile-point as-
semblages is needed before we can determine
whether occupation of the Front Range was continuous during the Altithermal interval.

[20] *The possibility of continuing contact with
eastern Wyoming, where James Allen and related
projectile-point styles were important prior
to the Altithermal, is particularly interesting. If the source of the quartzite and brown
chert is correctly identified, future excavations in the Spanish Diggings area should produce parallel-oblique-flaked projectile points
of Altithermal age.*

4 Excavations at the Ptarmigan Site (5 BL 170)

Introduction

The Ptarmigan site (5 BL 170) is a multiple-component Archaic campsite 350 m southwest of the Fourth of July Valley site, at an altitude of 3460 m. Its coordinates are 40°00'18" north latitude, 105°40'28" west longitude. The site was discovered and recorded in 1972 by William and Robert Benedict. Artifacts found on the ground surface were sparse and fragmentary; their apparent Archaic age and their relationship to the moraine and rock-glacier sequence (Figs. 7, 13) suggested that the site might provide information complementary to that already obtained from site 5 BL 120. We excavated the Ptarmigan site during the summers of 1973, 1974, and 1975. This chapter is a final site report.

Environment

The occupation area (Figs. 74, 75) is on a well-drained bedrock bench south of the North Fork of Middle Boulder Creek. It is 15 m higher than the stream, and shielded from it by a fringe of trees (Fig. 76). The bench is overlain by a veneer of glacial till that thickens northward and eastward, becoming a well-defined terminal moraine just north of the excavation area. This is the inner of three terminal moraines in the Fourth of July valley study area, and is the type locality for the Ptarmigan advance.

Several other sites occur along the bench (Fig. 13), which is an easy route for travelers bound for the upper valley and Arapaho Pass. A trickle of meltwater in the stone pavement at the front of the nearest rock glacier is a source of drinking water during the summer snow-free season. Krummholz spruce and fir trees north of the site (Figs. 74, 76)

provide fuel for fires. Although the occupation area offers no natural shelter, trees may have been present during former periods of favorable climate.

Winter snow accumulation is heavy at the site (Figs. 77, 78); dates for emergence of the excavation area between 1974 and 1980 ranged from July 6 to August 1. Lichen-kill caused by snowbank expansion during Audubon time is

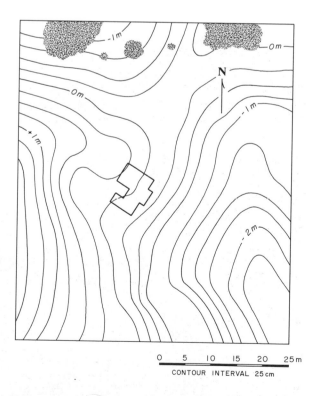

Figure 74. Topographic map of the Ptarmigan site. A permanent benchmark in the excavation area was assigned an elevation of 0.0 m. Tree islands are stippled.

Figure 75. View of the Ptarmigan site (5 BL 170). Sediments from rock glaciers in the background have been diverted eastward (left), away from the excavation area, by a shallow intervening swale. September 7, 1974.

Figure 76. View of the Ptarmigan site, looking south. The excavation area (arrow) is on a bedrock bench blanketed with ground moraine. Trees at the left edge of the photograph grow on a terminal moraine of Ptarmigan age. Two generations of rock glacier separate the excavation area from bedrock cliffs to the south. September 3, 1979.

Figure 77. Late winter view of the Ptarmigan site, looking eastward toward Arapaho Col. Site 5 BL 120 is buried by a dune of snow at the front of the most distant lobate rock glacier. The Ptarmigan site is north of the re-entrant between the two nearest rock glacier lobes. April 27, 1970.

Figure 78. Springtime view of the Ptarmigan site, looking southwest. A figure kneels at the location of the excavation area, which normally remains snow-covered until mid or late July. May 28, 1974.

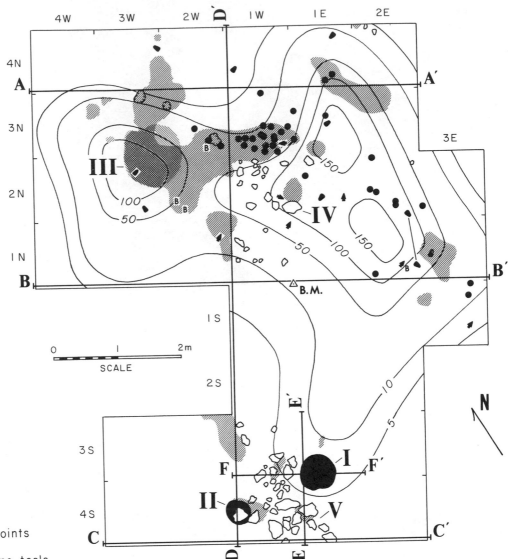

Projectile points

Chipped-stone tools

Milling slab fragments

B Bone

Oxidized (burned) rocks

Oxidized (burned) earth

Charcoal

Charcoal-filled basin

Shallow-basin hearth

5 Flakes per m²

Figure 79. Map of the Ptarmigan site, showing the locations of artifacts, bone fragments, charcoal accumulations, hearths, and burned rocks. Features are identified with Roman numerals; contours show the distribution of chipping debris; heavy lines mark the locations of profile drawings.

indicated by a sparse (10-40%) lichen cover; recolonization of the occupation area began about 1340 years ago, the age of a 54-mm *R. geographicum* thallus (Fig. 14).

Vegetation at the site is a mosaic of snow-tolerant plant communities dominated by species such as *Sibbaldia procumbens*, *Erigeron melanocephalus*, *Carex pyrenaica*, *Juncus drummondii*, *Artemisia scopulorum*, *Deschampsia caespitosa*, and *Vaccinium scoparium*. The little clubmoss, *Selaginella densa*, and the white, crust-forming soil lichen, *Lepraria arctica*, are important in several communities. The snow buttercup, *Ranunculus adoneus*, is an aspect dominant in mid summer, emerging from beneath its cover of winter snow with flowers fully formed. *Bistorta bistortoides*, *Erigeron perigrinus*, and *Castilleja rhexifolia* bloom in the excavation area later in the growing season.

The site is named for a family of ptarmigan that foraged past the excavation area almost every morning during the summer of 1974.

Field Procedures

Forty-three 1 m × 1 m grid squares were excavated at the site (Fig. 79). Excavation was by 2.5-cm levels within natural stratigraphic units. Material removed in troweling was screened through ¼-inch (6.4 mm) hardware cloth. Balks at the southwest and northwest sides of grid squares were drawn and described — then carefully troweled so that the positions of flakes could be plotted on the profile drawings. Thirty selected meters of stratigraphy (Fig. 80) illustrate the range of geologic deposits at the site and the relationship of radiocarbon-dated charcoal concentrations to the geologic sequence. The locations of artifacts, hearths, redeposited charcoal, oxidized stones, bone fragments, and concentrations of chipping debris are shown in figure 79.

Twenty-four soil samples were analyzed by the Front Range Environmental Laboratory, Fort Collins (Fig. 81). The analyses are internally consistent, and are useful in interpreting site stratigraphy; however, interlaboratory differences prevent comparison with Colorado State University textural analyses from site 5 BL 120.

Stratigraphy, Cultural Features, and Geologic History

INTRODUCTION

The 30 meters of profile wall shown in figure 80 show a degree of complexity that would never have been suspected from a single soil profile or test pit. Four transport agencies have influenced the deposits. Glacial ice has contributed coarse, bouldery till, gathered from source areas southwest of the site. Flowing water has reworked the till in a shallow swale at the south end of the excavation area (Fig. 74). Frost creep and slopewash have transported sediments from the eroded knoll northwest of the site. And wind, on at least two occasions, has blanketed the site with silt and fine sand.

I had hoped to find evidence for the arrival of nearby rock glaciers (Figs. 75-78) in the radiocarbon-dated sequence of deposits. Dates for the rock glaciers would have been useful in interpreting the glacial and climatic history of the valley. However, no sediments from either generation of rock glacier could be positively identified; the failure of sediments from these sources to reach the excavation area is attributed to the southeasterly slope of the intervening terrain.

Five stratigraphic units, several erosion surfaces, a well-developed oxidation profile, and a modern turf horizon are present at the site. Archeological features include two basin hearths, an open fireplace, and two accumulations of burned rock. These are described in the following pages, beginning with the oldest. Five radiocarbon dates provide chronologic control.

GLACIAL TILL

Till at the base of the stratigraphic sequence is light olive brown (2.5Y 5/3-5/4 m) to olive brown (2.5Y 4/3-4/4 m) in color, with a bouldery, gravelly loamy sand or gravelly sandy loam texture (Fig. 81). The unit is poorly sorted and non-stratified, firmer than overlying material, and weakly blocky. Stones are subangular (67.4%), subrounded (26.1%), and angular (6.5%); the undersurfaces of many are stained purplish black by manganese oxides or organic compounds. Thin caps of silt and clay occur on the tops of boulders and cobbles. The unit contains no cultural material or charcoal, and virtually no organic matter (Fig. 81).

A peculiar feature of the till, observed only at the south end of the excavation area, is its irregular upper surface, with as much as 40 cm of relief within a single 1 m × 1 m grid square (Fig. 82 a). Possible explanations are (1) melting of buried ice, such as occurred at site 5 BL 120; (2) soft-sediment deformation, such as is involved in the formation of load

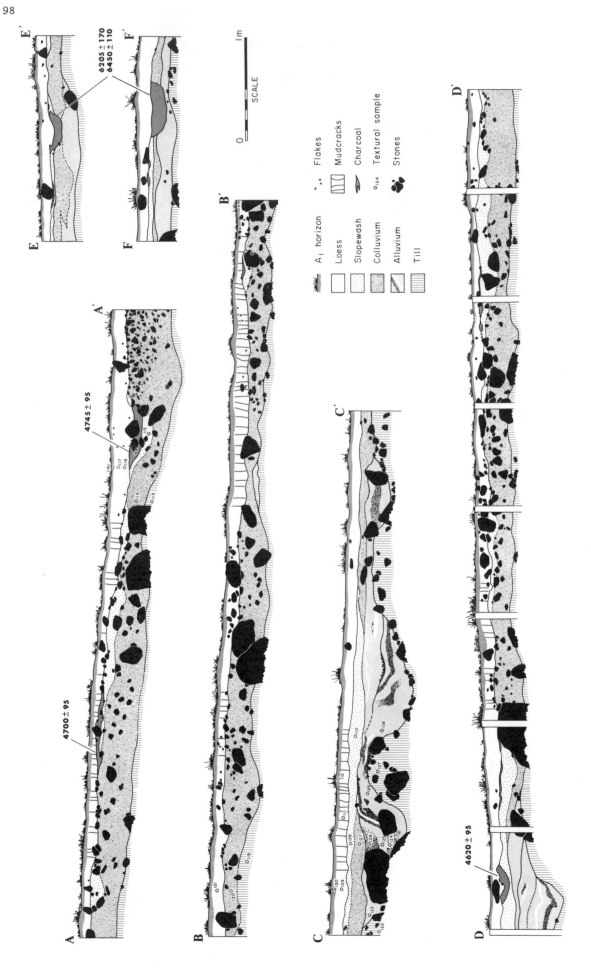

Figure 80. Selected stratigraphic profiles, site 5 BL 170. Profile locations are shown in figure 79; stratigraphic units are described in the text. Profiles A-A', B-B', C-C', and F-F' are south-wall drawings, reversed in drafting so that west is on the left and east is on the right.

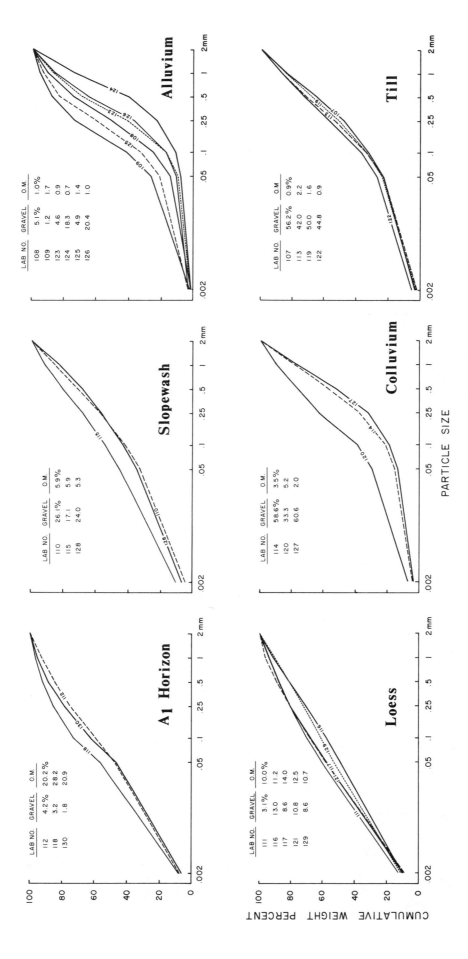

Figure 81. Textural analyses and organic-matter determinations, site 5 BL 170. Sample locations are indicated in figure 80.

casts and certain kinds of patterned ground; and (3) erosion by a small, meandering stream. Alternatives 1 and 2 appear to be most plausible: bedding planes in the channel fill dip so steeply (Fig. 80, C-C') that they have almost certainly undergone post-depositional deformation.

B-horizon oxidation ceases abruptly at the upper surface of the till in many grid squares. A stain of illuvial humus or a layer of yellowish brown (10YR 5/6 m) to strong brown (7.5YR 4/8 m) oxidized soil at the contact suggests that downward translocation of iron and organic matter has stopped at this depth because of the relative impermeability of the till. This is the primary reason for the variability of B-horizon thicknesses in the excavation area (20-55 cm).

The till is older than 6380 ± 95 BP, the weighted average age of charcoal from the oldest hearth at the site, and is younger than the inner of two Satanta Peak moraines. An age of approximately 6600-7250 radiocarbon years is suggested by weathering-rind development in quartz diorite cobbles (p. 45).

ALLUVIUM

Stratified sands and gravels in the southern part of the excavation area were deposited by flowing water. Sorting is moderate to good; organic-matter content is uniformly low (Fig. 81). Color, texture, structure, and consistence vary between the extremes described in the following paragraphs.

The coarsest-textured alluvial strata are dark yellowish brown (10YR 4/4 m) to olive brown (2.5Y 4/4 m) fine to very coarse sands. The sands are loose and structureless, drying rapidly and collapsing on exposure to air; pebbles are predominantly subangular, and are 2 cm or less in length. Pockets of magnetite-rich sand occur locally.

The finest-textured strata are light olive brown (2.5Y 5/3 m) to olive brown (2.5Y 4/3 m) loamy sands, without appreciable gravel (Fig. 81). Individual aggregates can be handled without breaking, but "pop" when squeezed; silt-rich lenses dry slowly and stand in relief, giving the profile wall a ribbed appearance after an hour or two of exposure. Structure is strongly platy. Vesicles as large as 2 mm are present; vesicle interiors are locally oxidized dark yellowish brown (10YR 4/6 m).

Two intervals of alluvial deposition, separated by an interval of erosion, are recognizable near the center of profile C-C' (Fig. 80). Bedding in the lower alluvial unit is more-or-less parallel to the irregular surface of the underlying till. The simplest explanation for this unit is that it was deposited during glacier retreat, and represents local reworking of the till by meltwater. The possibility that it is outwash from the rock glacier cannot be eliminated,

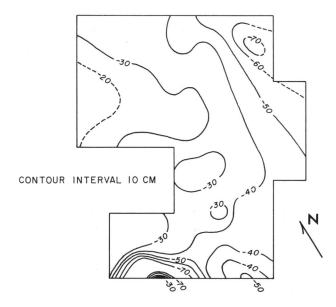

CONTOUR INTERVAL 10 CM

a. Topography of the glacial till surface (B.M. = 0 cm).

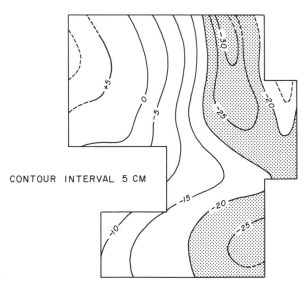

CONTOUR INTERVAL 5 CM

b. Topography of the occupation surface (B.M. = 0 cm).

Figure 82. Contour maps of important stratigraphic surfaces at the Ptarmigan site. Note (a) the deeply-channeled surface of the till at the south edge of the excavation area, caused by ice-core melting or load casting, and (b) the slope of the 4690-year occupation surface, down which artifacts and charcoal were transported by mass-wasting processes to an accumulation basin (stippled) in the northeast corner of the excavation area.

but seems unlikely due to local topographic factors. Transport distances were short, as indicated by the angularity of clasts. Steeply-dipping bedding planes imply post-depositional disturbance; the cause of the disturbance is unknown, but may relate to ice-core melting or soft-sediment deformation.

Erosion is indicated by an angular unconformity. Small stones have accumulated in depressions on the erosion surface (Fig. 80, profile C-C').

Bedding in the upper alluvial unit is conformable with the erosion surface on which it was deposited. The unit merges upward and northward into unstratified colluvium, suggesting a gradual shift, in time and space, from deposition by water to deposition by mass-wasting processes.

The lower part of the alluvium is a IVCox horizon. The upper part, at depths of less than 35-50 cm, is a IVB3 horizon.

COLLUVIUM

Colluvium in the excavation area ranges from dark yellowish brown (10YR 4/4-4/8 m) to strong brown (7.5YR 4/6-4/8 m) in color. It is a bouldery, gravelly sand, gravelly loamy sand, or gravelly sandy loam IIIB2 horizon (Fig. 81), distinguished from the till beneath it by its lack of compaction and the orientation of its clasts. The unit is poorly sorted and finely vesicular, commonly with weak to moderate blocky structure.

Stones in the colluvium are subangular (71.4%), subrounded (23.8%), and angular (4.8%), similar to stones in the underlying till. The undersurfaces of many stones are stained deep purple by manganese oxides or organic pigments; pebbles and cobbles locally show subhorizontal preferred orientations. Pieces of charcoal occur infrequently, and are associated with silty zones that have experienced mixing by frost processes; cultural material is absent. In several parts of the site (such as the east end of profile A-A', Fig. 80), there is evidence of frost sorting; here the unit is divisible into a very stony, gravelly upper facies and a stone-poor, sandy lower facies.

The upper boundary of the colluvium is an erosion surface, marked in some parts of the site by a lag accumulation of stones. This is the principal textural discontinuity in the stratigraphic sequence; it separates predominantly stony sediments (below) from predominantly fine-textured sediments (above).

The colluvium consists of till that has been reworked by frost processes and transported downslope for short distances by mass wasting. Lateral movement cannot have been great, as indicated by the failure of stony colluvial sediments to completely override fine-grained alluvium in the southern part of the excavation area (Fig. 80, profiles C-C', D-D'). The unit was deposited prior to 6380 ± 95 BP, under conditions that were relatively cool and moist, and is unlikely to be much younger than alluvium at the site.

OCCUPATION

Initial occupation of the site is recorded by Feature I (Fig. 79), a steep-sided basin hearth at the boundary between grid squares 3S/1E and 4S/1E. The basin was irregularly circular in plan view, measuring 55 × 55 cm, and had a maximum depth of 14 cm. Its fill was a mixture of abundant large charcoal fragments and small quantities of dark brown (10YR 4/3 m) and dark yellowish brown (10YR 4/4 m) silty earth. Widely scattered oxidized pebbles occurred in the hearth fill; there were no large stones, flakes, or artifacts. The upper boundary of the hearth was diffuse due to upfreezing of charcoal granules; the lower boundary was abrupt, marked by a thin, yellowish red (5YR 3/6 m) oxidation layer. Dates for replicate charcoal samples from the hearth are 6450 ± 110 BP (I-7458) and 6205 ± 170 BP (I-10,976), giving a weighted average age of 6380 ± 95 radiocarbon years.

The basin appeared, at first, to have been dug from an erosion surface at the top of a thin slopewash deposit (Fig. 80, profiles E-E', F-F'); pieces of charcoal from this and a younger occupation were scattered on the erosion surface. However, charcoal fragments also occurred *within* the slopewash and *in two small concentrations along its contact with the underlying colluvium*. Because disturbance processes at the site are incapable of displacing charcoal downward and concentrating it at a stratigraphic boundary, I now consider it likely that the basin was dug from the surface of the colluvium; charcoal was later upfrozen into the slopewash deposit and scattered on its surface by erosion. According to this interpretation, Feature I provides a maximum age for loess-rich slopewash at the site; regardless of *which* interpretation is correct, it gives a minimum age for the colluvium and till.

SLOPEWASH

Depressions in the eroded upper surface of the colluvium are filled with reworked loess. The deposit is a IIB2 horizon, dark yellowish brown (10YR 4/4-4/8 m) to dark brown (7.5YR 4/4 m) in color, with a sandy loam or gravelly sandy loam texture. Gravel is predominantly pea-sized, making the unit easy to recognize in troweling. Stones are uncommon. The deposit is siltier and less gravelly than underlying sediments; moderate to strong platy or blocky structure are characteristic, as is the presence of fine spherical vesicles.

The unit is interpreted as an admixture of loess and coarse clastic material, deposited in natural depressions by slopewash and related processes. It is believed to be of Altithermal age. Flecks of charcoal occur throughout the deposit, distributed so evenly at all depths that they suggest reworking of an older charcoal concentration. One possible source for the charcoal is Feature I, described in the preceding section.

A similar deposit at site 5 BL 120 is older than about 5960 radiocarbon years (Chapter 3). If the deposits are correlative, and if my in-

terpretation of the stratigraphic context of
Feature I is correct, average radiocarbon
ages of 6380 and 5960 years bracket an interval of loess deposition and slopewash activity.

SOIL FORMATION

Much of the bright B-horizon oxidation
observed in slopewash and colluvial sediments
at the site is likely to have occurred during
the latter part of the Altithermal. Elsewhere
in the Indian Peaks, a prominent soil has been
dated between about 5800 and 5300 radiocarbon
years BP (Benedict and Olson 1978, Burns
1979).

RE-OCCUPATION OF THE SITE

Two hearths and numerous other charcoal
concentrations originated at an erosional unconformity between slopewash or colluvial sediments and loess (Fig. 80). These features
and associated cultural material record a second visit to the site, about 4690 ± 55 radiocarbon years ago, the average age of three
dated charcoal samples.

Feature II was a basin hearth at the
boundary between grid squares 4S/1W and 4S/2W
(Fig. 79). Circular in outline, the basin measured 36 × 36 cm, and had a maximum depth of
17 cm. Its fill consisted of large wood charcoal fragments, with minor inclusions of
brown (10YR 3/3 m) to yellowish brown (10YR
5/4 m) silty earth and a few small oxidized
pebbles, 2 cm or less in maximum dimension.
The charcoal was underlain by a very thin layer of dark reddish brown (5YR 3/4 m) oxidized
soil. The hearth was dug from the eroded surface of dark yellowish brown gravelly, loessal
slopewash sediments (Fig. 80, profile D-D'),
and was overlain by 10 cm of dark brown loess.
A date of 4620 ± 95 BP (I-8562) was obtained
for charcoal from its fill. No cultural material was directly associated.

Feature III was an open fireplace on the
buried erosion surface in grid squares 2N/3W
and 3N/3W (Fig. 79). The erosion surface
transected dark yellowish brown loess-rich
slopewash sediments and colluvium, and was
sealed from the modern ground surface by a
layer of dark brown loess, 6 to 16 cm thick
(Fig. 80, profile A-A'). The location of the
fireplace was indicated by a circular patch of
strong brown (7.5YR 4/8 m) oxidized soil; the
radiocarbon age of associated charcoal was
4700 ± 95 years (I-8563). Feature III was at
the center of an important concentration of
chipping debris (Fig. 79), the significance of
which is discussed later in the report. A tool
fragment of white chert, an obsidian graver,
and a flake of volcanic glass were among items
found at the periphery of the hearth. Charcoal
from the hearth contained small, unidentifiable, calcined bone fragments (Fig. 79).

Much of the charcoal in the northeast
quarter of the excavation area appears to have
washed or blown from Feature III prior to burial of the occupation surface. A map of the occupation surface (Fig. 82 b) suggests a prob-

able explanation: the slope is easterly, leading from the hearth to a natural sediment trap
in which the charcoal has accumulated. A date
for redeposited charcoal from grid square
4N/1E is 4745 ± 95 BP (I-8280).

Associated with Feature III were three
small, steep-sided basins (Fig. 79), thought
to be the molds of boulders removed from the
occupation surface by its prehistoric inhabitants. An absence of oxidation suggests that
charcoal in the basins was redeposited, and did
not burn in place.

Feature IV was an accumulation of oxidized, angular cobbles and small boulders centered
in grid squares 1N/1W and 2N/1W (Fig. 79). The
stones appear to have been upfrozen from the
4690-year-old occupation surface; their bases
were at depths of 5 to 15 cm. Thirty to forty
percent of the flakes in these grid squares
showed evidence of crazing and pot-lid spalling,
a higher percentage than was found elsewhere at
the site. The rocks and flakes are likely to
have been cleared from Feature III, or from another fireplace in the vicinity.

Feature V was a concentration of burned
cobbles and boulders in grid squares 3S/1W,
4S/1W, and 4S/1E (Fig. 79). The bases of the
stones rested in loess at depths of 6 to 15 cm.
Most were underlain by layers of frost-sorted
sand and fine gravel containing charcoal granules; miniature sorted polygons were present
beneath several of the stones (Fig. 83). The
stones appear to have been cleared from one or
the other of two shallow-basin hearths in the
vicinity (Fig. 79).

Figure 83. Miniature sorted polygons exposed by removing a boulder from loess, grid
square 4S/1W. The polygons have the same
shapes and horizontal dimensions (3-5 cm) as
nonsorted mudcrack polygons in the loess;
their borders are filled with frost-sorted
coarse sand, fine gravel, and charcoal granules. A 15-cm rule provides scale.

LOESS

Re-occupation of the site was followed by deposition of humus-rich loess, similar to the loess that overlies the occupation surfaces at sites 5 BL 120 (Fig. 58, unit A-4) and 5 BL 154 (Fig. 29, A3 horizon). The loess is a dark brown (10YR 3/3 m) to dark yellowish brown (10YR 3/4-4/4 m) loam or sandy loam, coarsening downward. It is finely vesicular, with weak to moderate fine platy structure. Charcoal flecks, chipping debris, and artifacts occur throughout the deposit, but are most numerous near its base and in areas where there is dense underlying charcoal.

The unit is an A3 or B1 horizon. Pale colors in a 2- to 5-cm-thick layer directly beneath the turf suggest incipient E-horizon development in several parts of the excavation area.

The loess is younger than 4690 ± 55 BP, the average age of charcoal on the upper occupation surface. If correlation with the upper loess unit at site 5 BL 154 (Fig. 29) is correct, an age of less than 3385 ± 95 radiocarbon years (I-11,134) is indicated.

A1 HORIZON

The excavation area is sealed from modern erosive processes by a very dark brown (10YR 2/2-2/3 m) to dark brown (10YR 3/3 m) humus-rich A1 or 0 horizon, developed beneath rushes, sedges, herbs, and soil lichens. The A1 horizon is texturally similar to the loess in which it has developed, except that (1) smaller quantities of gravel have entered the unit from below, and (2) the cumulative grain-size curves (Fig. 81) suggest enrichment in very fine sand, probably blown to the site in recent centuries. The unit dries dark grayish brown (10YR 4/2 d) soon after exposure. It is matted with roots, and rich in organic matter (Fig. 81). Chipping debris and artifacts are present, but uncommon.

Artifacts

Artifacts from the Ptarmigan site are badly burned and fragmentary. Included are 11 broken projectile points, 3 triangular bifaces, an irregular flake cutting or scraping tool, a well-made scraper-plane, an obsidian graver, a split-pebble scraper, a spokeshave, 1362 flakes (including 42 with utilized edges), 42 sandstone milling-slab fragments, and 4 pieces of a broken cobble handstone. The locations of artifacts found during excavation are shown in figure 79. The tool assemblage suggests a variety of activities, including butchering, tool manufacture, tool repair, and grinding of plant foods, bone, or dried meat. Because of mixture by frost processes, artifacts could not be assigned to either of the two periods of occupation based on vertical stratigraphy. However, several of the tools were made of distinctive rock types that could be related to hearthside activity areas in which implements of the same rock types were resharpened. One of the activity areas was datable directly — the others inferentially — allowing tentative ages to be assigned to the bulk of the chipped-stone tool collection.

PROJECTILE POINTS

Corner-Notched, Convex Base (7 specimens, Fig. 84 a-g).

Tip. No data.

Blade. Blade shape uncertain due to wear and breakage. Both faces are fully flaked except for one specimen (Fig. 84 a), which retains a small unmodified area.

Shoulders. Abruptly sloping to oblique.

Hafting Area. Unground. Crushing is evident in several of the notches.

Stem. Expanding to greatly expanding.

Base. Slightly convex to convex. Unground to heavily ground.

Cross-Section. Bi-convex in transverse and longitudinal section.

Dimensions. Length N.D., width 19-22 mm, hafting width 12-15 mm, thickness 6.0-6.1 mm.

Rock Types. Chert/chalcedony (3), silicified wood (2), quartzite (2).

Provenience. a, mid-section from 2N/1W, 8½-cm depth; two other fragments from 2N/1E flake collection. b, 1S/3E, 2½-5 cm depth. c, 2N/1E, 6-cm depth. d, 2N/1E, reassembled from three fragments in flake collection. e, 1N/2E, 10-12½ cm depth. f, surface. g, 1N/1W, 2-cm depth. Reassembled fragments of broken corner-notched points (Fig. 84 a, d) were separated by distances of 1 m or less.

Wear. Blunting, crushing, and step flaking on the blade edges of the three largest specimens suggest secondary use as hafted butchering tools; transverse fractures are similarly worn.

Age. Four of the points (Fig. 84 d-g) are made of rock types that were associated with Feature III, an open fireplace dated at 4700 ± 95 BP (I-8563), and with Activity Area A.

Side-Notched, Very Slightly Convex Base (1 specimen, Fig. 84 h).

Tip. No data.

Blade. Original shape uncertain due to breakage and re-use. Flaking complete and bifacial.

Shoulders. One abrupt, one oblique.

Hafting Area. Unground.

Figure 84. Projectile points from the Ptarmigan site. *a-g*, corner-notched points. *h*, side-notched point. *i-k*, unclassifiable point fragments.

Stem. Greatly expanding.

Base. Very slightly convex. Lightly ground.

Cross-Section. Bi-convex in transverse section. Probably bi-convex in longitudinal section.

Dimensions. Length N.D., width 25 mm, hafting width 17 mm, thickness 4.5 mm.

Rock Type. Silicified wood (1).

Provenience. Base and majority of blade from grid square 3N/1W, 5-cm depth; remainder of blade from 3N/2W flake collection. Fragments were separated from each other by a distance of approximately 1 m.

Wear. Rounding is the principal form of edge wear on the surviving original blade edge. Broken edges show crushing, step flaking, and rounding due to heavy use.

Age. Resharpening flakes of the same distinctive silicified wood formed a tight cluster in grid square 2N/2E, and were part of Activity Area B. Area B is related by shared rock types to Feature I, a hearth with a weighted average age of 6380 ± 95 radiocarbon years.

Comment. The point is thinner and broader than others from the site. The base fragment shown in figure 84 *g* should perhaps be included in this group.

Unclassifiable Projectile-Point Fragments (3 specimens, Fig. 84 *i-k*).

A projectile point tip (Fig. 84 *i*) found at 9-cm depth in grid square 1N/2W is made of gray silicified wood; its original and broken edges are lightly worn by use. Two unclassifiable projectile-point bases were found on the ground surface; both are made of yellowish brown silicified wood. The smaller fragment (Fig. 84 *j*) has a hafting width of 9 mm, and shows very light basal grinding; a similar point base is illustrated by Jennings (1980, Fig. 17 *t*). The larger fragment (Fig. 84 *k*) has a slightly expanding stem and an irregularly convex, very lightly ground base; its hafting width is 12 mm, and its thickness 4.7 mm.

OTHER CHIPPED-STONE TOOLS

Biface (Fig. 85 *a*). The tip of a bifacial knife, made of yellowish brown chert, was found at 13-cm depth in grid square 2N/2E. The remainder of the biface, oxidized dark red by burning, was found 78 cm to the south, at 15-cm depth in grid square 1N/2E. Neither tool fragment shows evidence of utilization after breakage. The tool is thought to have functioned as a backed knife, with pressure applied to a plane striking platform that was allowed to remain on one lateral edge (Fig. 85 *a*). The blade edge opposite the striking platform has

Figure 85. Chipped-stone tools from the Ptarmigan site. *a-c*, bifaces. *d*, flake knife or scraper. *e*, scraper-plane on prismatic flake. *f*, flake graver. *g*, split-pebble scraper. *h*, spokeshave. *i-l*, unclassifiable tool fragments. S.P. = striking platform. C = cortex.

been used most heavily (blunting and step flaking), and shows evidence of resharpening. Edge angles range from 30° to 40° along this margin of the tool.

Triangular Biface (Fig. 85 b). A small, triangular biface, made from a flake of light gray chalcedony with opaque, white, spherical inclusions, was found on the ground surface. Retouch is complete on one face, and partial (ca. 75%) on the other. Working edges are gently convex; edge angles vary from 30° to 45° along lateral edges, and from 60° to 65° along the transverse edge. Edge wear includes rounding, blunting, and step flaking, which occur around the entire periphery of the tool; surface wear is absent.

Biface (Fig. 85 c). The largest biface from the site is made from a curved flake of fine-grained light brownish gray quartzite. Flaking is complete on both faces, producing a symmetrical tool with slightly convex working edges and rounded corners. Edge angles vary from 35° to 55°. Rounding, blunting, and step flaking occur on all edges; the ridges between flake scars are rounded, as are other high spots on the blade, suggesting deep penetration during use as a cutting tool. Provenience: surface.

Irregular Flake Knife or Scraper (Fig. 85 d). One edge of an irregularly-shaped flake of dark brown chert, found 15 cm beneath the ground surface in grid square 4N/1E, shows evidence of use, and probably of deliberate unifacial retouch. The tool is easily held between thumb and forefinger. Its 40°-70° working edge would have been suitable for a variety of functions. Edge wear consists of rounding, blunting, and step flaking.

Scraper-Plane on Prismatic Flake (Fig. 85 e). This well-made tool, found at 3- to 4-cm depth in grid square 4N/1W, is made from a prismatic blade of excellent-quality yellowish brown to light olive brown chert with black dendritic inclusions. The blade is parallel-sided, with a concave ventral surface and a trapezoidal cross section. Modification is limited to steep unifacial retouch of its thick distal end (producing a working edge angle of 60°-70°), and to partial unifacial retouch of its lateral edges. Step flaking and blunting characterize the transverse working edge; lateral edges show a tendency toward rounding, although other forms of wear are also present. The tool may have been hafted for use, judging from the occurrence of polish along flake ridges on its dorsal surface.

Flake Graver (Fig. 85 f). Volcanic glass is a rarity in the Indian Peaks; an obsidian graver from 12-cm depth in grid square 2N/3W is one of fewer than a dozen pieces of this material found during our site surveys and excavations. The tool is made from a small expanding flake with a worn striking platform.

One lateral edge of the flake is retouched unifacially (dorsal side) along its entire length. A notch in the flake's steep transverse hinge fracture completes the graving tip. The notch was produced by fine bifacial pressure retouch. The tool is worn only slightly; step flaking and blunting are represented.

Split-Pebble Scraper (Fig. 85 g). A thick, wedge-shaped flake of grayish brown chalcedony with opaque white inclusions, found at 8-cm depth in grid square 4N/3W, has been modified for use as a hand-held scraping tool. The broad end of the wedge is the smooth, polished, outer surface of a nodule or stream pebble; the tapered end has been flaked bifacially to an angle of 60°-85°. Step flaking, rounding, and blunting are the principal forms of edge wear; surface wear is negligible. Concavities on both faces make the tool easy to grasp between thumb and forefinger.

Spokeshave (Fig. 85 h). Working of wood or bone is suggested by a spokeshave found 12 cm beneath the surface of grid square 3N/1E. The tool is made from a flake of olive brown chert with inclusions of druse quartz. Its ventral surface is naturally irregular, crossed by a shallow groove about 10 mm wide and 2 mm deep. Where the groove intersects the edge of the flake, a notch was produced by fine unifacial (dorsal) pressure retouch. The tool would have been suitable for smoothing a shaft of bone or wood with a diameter of approximately 1 cm. Edge wear consists of blunting and fine step flaking; polish occurs in the groove for a distance of several millimeters behind the working edge.

Unclassifiable Tool Fragments (Fig. 85 i-l). Four tool fragments are not described due to their small size and damage by burning. Proveniences and rock types are as follows:

i, 1N/3E, 12½-15 cm, red (burned) chert.
j, 2N/3W, 2½-5 cm, white chert.
k, 2N/1E, 9 cm, black (burned) silicified wood.
l, 2N/1W, gray (burned) chert, 4 pieces reassembled from flake collection.

UTILIZED FLAKES

Utilized flakes occurred in several discrete clusters (Fig. 86). Seven were found in the northeast corner of the excavation area, where cultural material has been redeposited by geologic processes. Utilized flakes from this part of the site (Fig. 87 a-g) are large, ranging from 25 to 43 mm in maximum length. They include a possible spokeshave (Fig. 87c), and two backed cutting tools (Fig. 87 f-g).

Thirteen utilized flakes occurred in a concentration centered on grid square 1N/2E (Fig. 87 h-t). These flakes are 14 to 40 mm in maximum dimension. One (Fig. 87 i) has been used as an end scraper, and another (Fig. 87 h) as a backed cutting tool; the pointed tip of a third (Fig. 87 j) is rounded by heavy use.

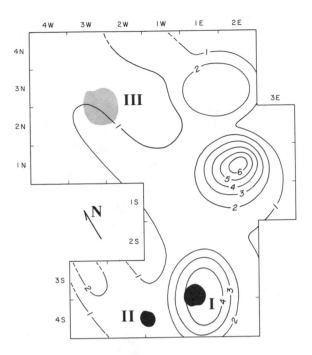

Figure 86. Distribution of utilized flakes. Contours indicate the number of utilized flakes per 1 m² excavation unit.

Five small curved flakes (Fig. 87 *m-q*) show fine utilization retouch (dorsal side only) along their distal edges.

Four utilized flakes of clear to white chalcedony with inclusions of opaque white chert (Fig. 87 *u-x*) were found in a linear scatter extending southward from a concentration of resharpening flakes at the periphery of Feature III. Lengths range from 11 to 21 mm. The smallest flake (Fig. 87 *v*) has an arcuate transverse working edge, steepened unifacially by use.

Utilized flakes were the *only* implements found in the southern part of the excavation area, where they occurred in two related concentrations (Fig. 86). Four (Fig. 87 *y-b'*) are from the southwest corner of the site, and fourteen (Fig. 87 *c'-p'*) from the periphery of Feature I. Maximum dimensions range from 7 to 28 mm. Included are several relatively large utilized flakes, similar to those in concentrations to the north. More characteristic of the southern part of the site, however, are miniature utilized flakes of brown chert and brown silicified wood (several varieties), some with a waxy luster suggestive of heat treatment. The utilized edges of all but one of these micro-tools were originally sharp (15°-35°); the exception (Fig. 87 *i'*) is a tabular flake of chalcedony bounded by utilized snap fractures.

The functions of micro-tools from the site are unknown. Handheld, the tiny sharp-edged flakes could have been used for delicate work in bone, wood, or hide.

The horizontal distribution of micro-tools suggests an association with Feature I (Fig. 86). One of the micro-tools (Fig. 87 *m'*) was found at 15-cm depth in loessal slopewash sediments, grid square 2S/1E, near the northern edge of Feature I. Its stratigraphic position suggests a relationship to the 6380-year-old component at the site.

CHIPPING DEBRIS

The collection of 1362 excavated flakes included 592 flakes with striking platforms. Of these, 518 had been detached from the dull, utilized edges of cutting and scraping tools, 36 had been detached from non-utilized edges, and 38 were of indeterminate origin. I conclude that tool manufacture occurred at the site, but was a minor activity in comparison to the resharpening of tools that had been manufactured elsewhere.

Among the resharpening flakes, 34 distinctly different rock types were present, including 22 varieties of chert/chalcedony, 10 of silicified wood, 1 of quartzite, and 1 of volcanic glass. This is a minimum estimate of the number of tools resharpened in the excavation area: a conservative estimate that allows for only one tool of each rock type, and that assumes considerable lithologic variation within each tool.

Many of the flakes are burned. The principal concentration of burned flakes was associated with Feature IV, an accumulation of oxidized stones on the occupation surface north of the center of the excavation area.

Flake distribution maps were prepared for the 12 most distinctive and abundant rock types (Fig. 88). Together, these rock types account for 75.3% of the total flake collection and 76.4% of the resharpening flakes from the site. Each rock type has a unique lithology, is easily recognized, and is believed to have been quarried at a single source. Rock type 3, the most abundant lithic material, is chert from Middle or North Park; rock type 12 is silicified wood from the Denver Basin, near Parker, Colorado; other source areas have not yet been identified. The characteristics of each rock type are summarized in Appendix C.

Three distributional patterns are apparent. In the first pattern, shared by six rock types (Fig. 88, *1-6*), flakes occurred in two discrete areas: (1) in the vicinity of Feature III, the open fireplace in grid squares 2N/3W and 3N/3W; and (2) in a natural depression 3-4 m downslope (Fig. 82 b). These areas are interpreted, respectively, as (1) a primary activity area, where tools were resharpened at hearthside, and (2) a depositional basin, where flakes and charcoal were redeposited by slopewash, wind, and/or frost processes.

In the second distributional pattern, shared by five rock types (Fig. 88, *7-11*), flakes showed a single frequency maximum, centered in the vicinity of grid squares 2N/1E, 2N/2E, and 1N/2E. These flakes were also largely the result of tool resharpening. They are thought to indicate a second primary activity

108

Figure 87. Utilized flakes, Ptarmigan site. Note the marked decrease in average size between the northeast (*a-g*) and southeast (*c'-p'*) corners of the excavation area.

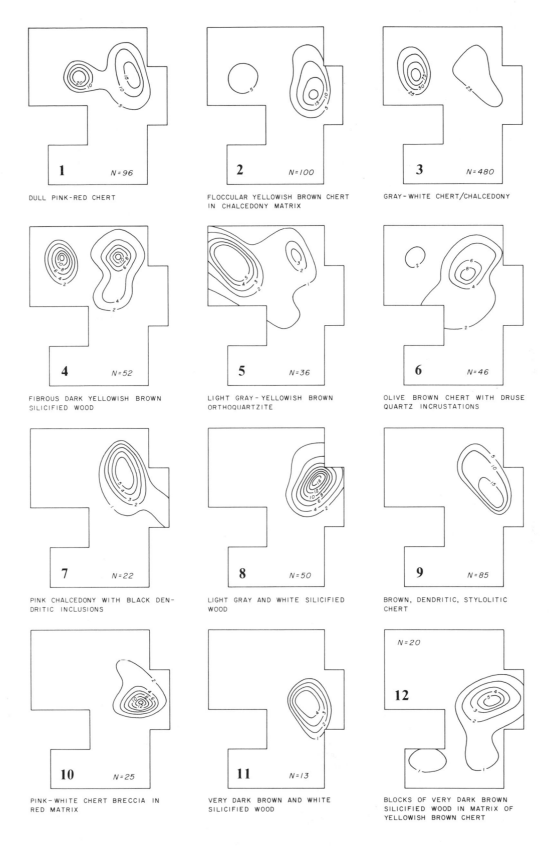

Figure 88. Distribution of principal rock types at the Ptarmigan site. Contours indicate the number of waste flakes of each rock type per 1 m² excavation unit. Rock-type descriptions are in Appendix C.

area; a less-likely possibility is that they have been transported by geologic processes from beyond the limits of our excavations.

A third distributional pattern, exhibited by only one rock type (Fig. 88, *12*), is similar to the second, except that flakes of this rock type also occurred in small numbers near hearths in the southern part of the excavation area. Both resharpening and manufacturing flakes (including 7 decortication flakes) were represented. Later in the paper I will discuss the importance of this rock type in linking activity areas at the site, and in developing an age estimate for the side-notched projectile-point component.

GRINDING TOOLS

Twenty-nine fragments of an arkosic sandstone milling slab (Fig. 89 *a*) were found in the excavation area, where they rested on the 4690-year-old occupation surface or were embedded in the overlying loess, their bases at depths of 8 to 17 cm. More than half of the pieces were recovered from grid square 3N/1W (Fig. 79); the remainder were scattered on the slope to the east, separated by distances as great as 4.1 m. The maximum thickness of the reconstructed slab is 24 mm. One surface is rough and irregular, the other polished and slightly dish-shaped due to use beneath a cobble handstone. Use striations trend parallel to the long axis of the reassembled slab. The sandstone is yellowish brown (10YR 5/4) to brown (7.5YR 5/4) in color, and is composed of moderately well sorted, medium to coarse quartz and feldspar sand grains with minor quantities of muscovite. Widely scattered subangular to subrounded pebbles as large as 9 mm are present; cementation is strong enough that the pebbles have been ground flush with the surface of the slab, rather than pulling free from the matrix during use. The sandstone is probably derived from a slabby facies of the Fountain arkose (Pennsylvanian-Permian), which outcrops in the Boulder area, 32 km east of the site.

Three fragments of a second sandstone milling slab were found in grid square 3N/2W, where they occurred in charcoal-rich loess, at depths of 7 to 16 cm. The slab was used bifacially, and has a maximum thickness of 16 mm. It is composed of well-sorted, silica-cemented, fine to medium quartz sand grains, and is derived from the Lyons Formation (Permian), which overlies the Fountain arkose in the foothills west of Boulder.

Ten fragments of a thin (10 mm) flat slab of Lyons sandstone found on the slope southeast of the excavation area may also relate to occupation of the Ptarmigan site, although this cannot be proven. Two of the fragments are smoothed and polished bifacially. Associated with the slab were four pieces of a well-made oval handstone, the largest of which is illustrated in figure 89 *b*. The handstone is made of Lyons sandstone, and was used bifacially. Its maximum thickness is 38 mm.

Activity Areas

Despite considerable vertical and horizontal redeposition of artifacts, discrete activity areas can be identified, tentatively dated, and assigned to one or the other of two components at the site. Figure 90 indicates the main parts of the site in which tools of distinctive rock types were resharpened and/or natural sharp-edged flakes were utilized. Capital letters designate activity areas. Areas in which flakes and artifacts have been concentrated by geologic processes are excluded from this discussion.

ACTIVITY AREA A

Activity Area A (Fig. 90) was centered around Feature III, an open fireplace with a radiocarbon age of 4700 ± 95 years. Associated with charcoal from the fireplace were scraps of unidentifiable burned bone. The fireplace was a center for tool resharpening. Among the rock types present were an even-grained gray to yellowish brown orthoquartzite, which oxidizes reddish brown when heated; a fibrous, dark yellowish brown silicified wood that oxidizes dusky red to black when heated; a grayish brown to white chert/chalcedony containing opaque white spherical inclusions; and an olive brown chert with internal fractures that are encrusted with druse quartz. Four fragmentary corner-notched projectile points (Fig. 84 *d-g*), two bifaces (Fig. 85 *b-d*), a split-pebble scraper (Fig. 85 *g*, a spokeshave (Fig. 85 *h*), and three unclassifiable tool fragments (Fig. 85 *j-l*) were made of these distinctive rock types. Although the tools were widely scattered across the site, all were presumably made by the people who resharpened implements of the same rock types in Activity Area A. An age of approximately 4700 radiocarbon years can be inferred for tools made of these rock types, and (with lesser confidence) for other tools that are typologically similar.

ACTIVITY AREA B

Activity Area B (Fig. 90) was centered in grid squares 2N/1E, 2N/2E, and 1N/2E. In addition to cultural material redeposited from higher on the slope, it contained five distinctive rock types that do not occur elsewhere at the site (Fig. 88, *7-11*). This suggests that it was a workshop area in its own right, or that it received redeposited material from an unexcavated workshop area to the east.

Among the rock types characteristic of Activity Area B was a distinctive gray and white silicified wood (rock type 8). The side-notched point illustrated in figure 84 was made of identical material, presumably by the people who resharpened tools in Activity Area B. Activity Areas A and B can be assigned with considerable confidence to the users of corner-notched and side-notched projectile points, respectively. Unfortunately, only Area A is ra-

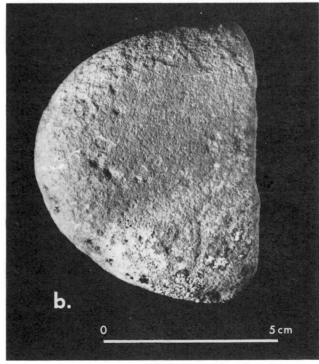

Figure 89. Grinding tools from the Ptarmigan site. *a*, sandstone milling slab, partially reassembled from excavated fragments; *b*, handstone fragment, found on the ground surface southeast of the excavation area.

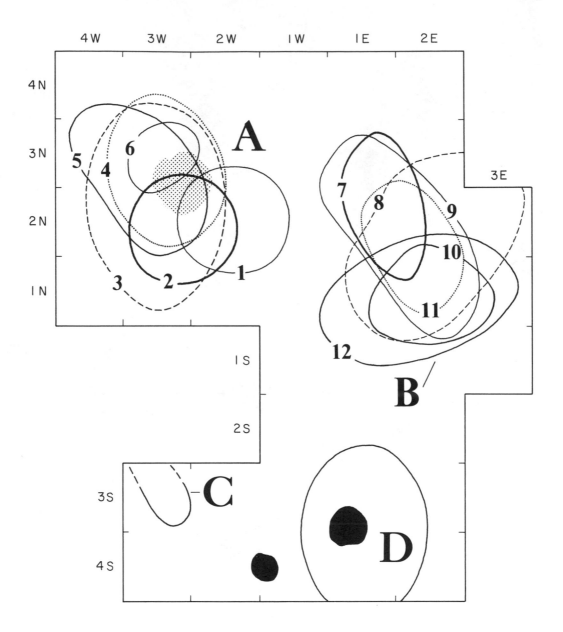

Figure 90. Activity areas at the Ptarmigan site, inferred from the distribution of distinctive rock types. Area A was a center of tool resharpening, and Area B a center of tool resharpening and manufacture. Corner-notched projectile points from the site were made of rock types 3-5, whose primary context lies in Area A. A side-notched point is made of rock type 8, which occurs exclusively in Area B. Areas C and D were characterized by miniature utilized flakes, primarily of heat-treated chert and silicified wood.

diocarbon dated.

Activity Area B was a center for tool resharpening and manufacture, as well as for cutting and scraping operations that involved the use of unmodified sharp-edged flakes (Fig. 86). Except for the side-notched projectile point, re-used as a hafted cutting tool, none of the tools resharpened in this part of the site were discarded locally. A tool made from a cortex-covered nodule of brown silicified wood (rock type 12) in Activity Area B — the only definite evidence of tool manufacture at the site — was apparently also carried away by its makers.

ACTIVITY AREAS C AND D

Activity Areas C and D, in the southern part of the excavation area, were not important centers of tool repair, although resharpening flakes occur in small numbers; there is no evidence for tool manufacture or plant-food preparation. The only artifacts are utilized flakes, the emphasis being upon miniature flakes that would have been suitable for delicate work in wood, bone, or hide. Both areas contain the same rock types (primarily dark brown heat-treated cherts and silicified woods), and are believed to have been used by the same people. A relationship to Feature I appears to be most probable (Fig. 90).

Activity Areas C and D are linked to Area B by the mutual occurrence of rock type 12 (Fig. 88). *If* Area D was a fireside workshop centered around Feature I (as suggested by Fig. 90), *if* Areas B and D were used by the same people (as suggested by the mutual occurrence of rock type 12), and *if* the projectile point shown in figure 84 *h* was made by the users of Area B (as suggested by the distribution of rock type 8), *then an age of about 6380 radiocarbon years can be assigned to the side-notched projectile point component at the site.* Alternately (or perhaps additionally), two unclassifiable projectile-point fragments from the site (Fig. 84 *j-k*) can perhaps be assigned to the 6380-yr-old component; both are made of yellowish-brown silicified wood, similar (but not identical) to rock type 12, and probably also from the Denver Basin.

ACTIVITY AREA E

Activity Area E, centered in grid square 3N/1W (Fig. 79), was a center for grinding seeds, roots, or dried meat. Fragments of two sandstone milling slabs were found in Area E. Pieces of the same slabs in other parts of the site may have been scattered by natural processes; however, the horizontal separation of matching fragments is greater than for other artifact classes, and in some cases violates local slope conditions, suggesting that large pieces of sandstone continued to be used in other parts of the site after the original slab had been broken.

Cultural Relationships

EARLY COMPONENT

Initial occupation of the site is dated at 6450 ± 110 BP (I-7458) and 6205 ± 170 BP (I-10,976). Related to this occupation is Feature I, a steep-sided basin hearth. *Possibly* related are the miniature utilized flakes from Activity Areas C and D, resharpening and manufacturing flakes from Area B (rock types 7 to 12), a side-notched projectile point made of gray and white silicified wood (Fig. 84 *h*), and two unclassifiable projectile-point fragments, both made of yellowish brown silicified wood.

The side-notched point is of a style seen rarely in the Colorado mountains. Fewer than half a dozen comparable points have been found at high altitudes in the Front Range; the style is also uncommon in the foothills, although small numbers of the points are reported from the lower levels of the LoDaisKa Rockshelter (Irwin and Irwin 1959).

Northward into Wyoming, the style becomes more abundant, occurring in Early Plains Archaic components at sites in the mountains and foothills; dates of 7685 ± 580 BP (UGa-957) to at least 5100 ± 330 BP (RL-675) are thought to apply (Frison 1978: 41-46). The point style is part of a typological continuum that existed, during the Altithermal, across much of the northern United States and southern Canada, from the Columbia Plateau and northern Great Basin (Bitterroot Side-notched, Northern Side-notched, and Elko Side-notched points) through the Central and Northern Rocky Mountains (Mummy Cave Side-notched points) to the Central Plains and Prairie Peninsula (Logan Creek and Simonsen Side-notched points). The style was present at the eastern margin of the Plains at least 8500 radiocarbon years ago, and may have originated in the eastern woodlands. Its scarcity in the Front Range is attributed to isolation of the region by environmental barriers, such as the Wyoming Basin and shortgrass plains (Benedict and Olson 1978: 147-148), and to the fact that a number of competing cultures were present in the Front Range during the Altithermal interval (Benedict 1979a).

LATE COMPONENT

Dates for re-occupation of the site are 4745 ± 95 BP (I-8280), 4700 ± 95 BP (I-8563), and 4620 ± 95 BP (I-8562). Related to this second period of occupation are Feature II, a shallow-basin hearth; Feature III, an open fireplace; resharpening flakes from Activity Area A; at least two triangular bifaces (Fig. 85 *b, c*); a spokeshave (Fig. 85 *h*); a split-pebble scraper (Fig. 85 *g*); three unclassifiable tool fragments (Fig. 85 *j-l*); and a series of seven fragmentary corner-notched projectile points (Fig. 84 *a-g*). If depressions in the upper occupation surface are the molds of stones gathered for use in cooking, Feature IV can probably be attributed to the younger component at

114

the site. Milling-slab fragments found down-slope from Feature III may also be associated, although this is unproven.

The corner-notched projectile points are stylistically similar to, and probably derived from, the Mount Albion Corner-notched style; they differ from it primarily in a lesser emphasis on basal and notch grinding. They are attributed to a local Archaic tradition that appeared in the Front Range during the latter part of the Altithermal (Benedict and Olson 1978), was present at Dipper Gap and Spring Gulch during late Triple Lakes time (Metcalf 1974, Kainer 1976), and persisted until at least 2000 or 1500 yr BP at sites such as Lo-DaisKa (Irwin and Irwin 1959), Magic Mountain (Irwin-Williams and Irwin 1966), Willowbrook (Leach 1966), Van Bibber Creek (C. Nelson 1969), and Coney Lake (Benedict 1973c).

debris suggest that butchering and tool repair were important activities during this period in the history of the site. A shallow-basin hearth and open fireplace were used, perhaps in conjunction with stones for cooking. If grinding implements from the excavation area relate to this component, which is unproven, processing of vegetal materials may also have been important.

The 4690-year occupation surface is overlain by loess, believed to be of late- or post-Triple Lakes age. Freeze-thaw processes have caused cultural material to move upward into this unit, blurring the stratigraphic relationships of artifacts, and making it necessary to assign them to their proper components by means of a tenuous procedure involving the association of distinctive rock types with dated activity areas. The occupation area was covered with late-lying snow during Audubon time, emerging about 1340 years ago. An A1 horizon at the site is probably of post-Audubon age.

Summary

The Ptarmigan site is geologically important because of the minimum age that it provides for the inner of three terminal moraines in the Fourth of July valley study area. Till at the site was deposited prior to 6380 ± 95 BP; its surface was deformed by ice-core melting soon after deglaciation. Areas of slumping became filled with younger sediments, which were deposited by flowing water at the southern margin of the excavation area, and by mass-wasting processes elsewhere.

The earliest visitors to the site, about 6380 ± 95 radiocarbon years ago, camped on the eroded surface of the alluvium and colluvium. An Early Plains Archaic hunting party with ties to the mountains and foothills north of the Wyoming Basin appears to have been represented, although evidence is scanty. Artifacts and waste flakes suggest brief occupation, perhaps involving secondary butchering, tool repair, and tool manufacture. A steep-sided basin hearth was used. The diagnostic projectile point was a side-notched form similar to points in the Bitterroot-Logan Creek continuum. This component brings to four the number of cultural complexes known to have been present above timberline in the Indian Peaks during the Altithermal.

Occupation was followed by an interval of loess deposition and slopewash. Cultural material was heaved to the surface by freezing and thawing. A periglacial climate is suggested.

About 4690 ± 55 radiocarbon years ago the site was visited by people with a long tradition of Front Range occupation. They camped briefly on an erosion surface cut in slopewash sediments and colluvium. The diagnostic projectile point was a corner-notched form, believed to be derived from the Mount Albion Corner-notched style. Artifacts and chipping

5

Paleoclimatic Summary

The purpose of Chapter 5 is to summarize and interpret paleoenvironmental data from glacial and archeological studies in the Fourth of July valley. No single valley can provide a complete chronology, nor can we assume that the sequence of glacial deposits on the floor of *this* valley is regionally representative. The entire North Fork drainage is currently under study; the chronology discussed here is a progress report on ongoing research.

LATE STADE, PINEDALE GLACIATION

Little can be said about the late stade of Pinedale Glaciation, which is represented in the study area only by patches of ground moraine and vast expanses of striated bedrock. Terminal deposits of late Pinedale age are 6-7 km downvalley from cirque headwalls, in the subalpine forest, at an altitude of 3000-3050 m; I have not studied these deposits in detail, and have no radiocarbon evidence to add to that provided by Madole (1976a, 1980a).

The entire upper Fourth of July valley, including south-facing slopes that were never again glaciated, contained snow and ice during late Pinedale time. This was the last true valley glaciation to affect the Front Range crest; subsequent ice advances were confined to narrow zones along the north-facing walls of valleys, and to cirques. None was longer than about 2 km.

SATANTA PEAK ADVANCES

Satanta Peak glaciers were small, and were restricted to topographic situations that inhibited summer melting. Close association with north-facing cliffs distinguishes them from Pinedale glaciers, which filled entire valleys, and from modern glaciers, which occur in cirques whose orientations and topographies favor concentration of snow by westerly winds. This suggests that summer temperatures had risen considerably by Satanta Peak time, but that snowfall was not yet in such critically short supply that its augmentation by wind-drifting had become essential.

Two Satanta Peak advances are recorded in the study area. The earliest and most extensive originated in a cirque south of Mount Neva and in snowfields along the southern margin of the study area. It flowed to the northeast, filling the bedrock trough that presently carries the main drainage of the North Fork of Middle Boulder Creek, and depositing a terminal moraine at an altitude of 3410 m.

The second advance originated in snowfields along the north-facing valley wall, and does not seem to have been physically connected to a glacier that occupied the cirque south of Mount Neva at this time. Although its terminal moraine is at an altitude of 3420 m, comparable to that of the early Satanta Peak advance, the total area covered by ice may have been only 60-70% as large.

Survival of an ice core in the early Satanta Peak moraine until the end of the late Satanta Peak advance — inferred from slump structures in outwash at site 5 BL 120 — is evidence that the cycle of glacier advance, retreat, and readvance was rapidly completed, and that the mid-Satanta Peak retreat phase was brief and relatively cool. Identical maximum weathering-rind thicknesses are further evidence that early and late Satanta Peak moraines and associated outwash are closely similar in age.

By 9215 ± 105 BP (I-11,092 avg.), Satanta Peak glaciers had withdrawn from the study area, the outer Satanta Peak moraine had been breached by stream erosion, and late Satanta Peak outwash had been dissected by the North Fork of Middle Boulder Creek. Loess overlying the outwash was reworked by frost or slopewash processes prior to 8270 ± 140 BP (I-11,127); the loess is likely to have been deposited during Satanta Peak deglaciation, when extensive areas of bare soil were exposed to wind erosion.

At Caribou Lake, 2 km to the northwest, Satanta Peak deposits are older than 9915 ± 165 radiocarbon years (I-6335, Benedict 1973a). An absence of suitable rock types in the Caribou Lake drainage prevents comparison of weathering-rind data between the two localities.

Beyond the Front Range, Satanta Peak till

may correlate with Hyak and Rat Creek moraines in the North Cascade Range (Porter 1978); with the Sumas readvance of the Cordilleran Ice Sheet in the Fraser Lowland (Armstrong *et al.* 1965); with part, or all, of the type Temple Lake moraine in the Wind River Mountains, Wyoming (Currey 1974, C. Miller and Birkeland 1974); and with Devils Castle till in Little Cottonwood Canyon, Utah (Madsen and Currey 1979). There is no proof, however, of precise synchroneity.

PTARMIGAN ADVANCE

The Ptarmigan advance of mid-Altithermal time was almost as extensive as the late Satanta Peak advance that preceded it. A source in shaded, north-facing snowfields suggests that summer temperatures continued to be relatively warm. Flow was in a northerly to north-northeasterly direction, and reached a minimum altitude of 3475 m. The glacier deposited a single, well-defined terminal moraine; the moraine is blocky, and consists of three distinctly arcuate segments, convex away from the glacier front.

Weathering-rind data suggest that the type Ptarmigan moraine was deposited about 7250-6600 radiocarbon years ago. These estimates assume that the inner Satanta Peak moraine, downvalley, is 11,000-10,000 radiocarbon years old, and that weathering-rind thicknesses increase as a linear function of time. If either assumption is incorrect, the dates will require adjustment. If weathering-rind thickness is a logarithmic function of time, for example, the age of the deposit will be younger. It cannot be younger than 6380 ± 95 BP, which is the weighted average age of replicate charcoal samples (I-7458, I-10,976) from an Early Archaic hearth on ground moraine of this advance.

The estimated age of the Ptarmigan moraine corresponds closely to the age of the Mazama Ash, which was deposited between about 7000 and 6600 radiocarbon years ago (Mehringer *et al.* 1977, Mack *et al.* 1978, 1979). Large volcanic eruptions that eject ash into the stratosphere can trigger glaciation by reducing incoming solar radiation, increasing the albedo of extensive land areas, and initiating various feedback mechanisms (Bray 1979). The eruptions of Mount Mazama, in the Cascade Range, produced thick and extensive ash deposits, and it is possible that the associated temperature decline triggered a glacial advance in the Indian Peaks timberline region. Palynological records are not generally sensitive enough to detect temperature changes as short-lived as those that may have accompanied the Mazama eruptions. However, in at least one study (Buchner 1980) there is evidence for a decline in mean July temperature coincident with deposition of the Mazama Ash.

Beyond the limits of the Front Range there is no substantiated record of Altithermal glaciation in western North America. Stalker (1969) obtained collagen dates of 6340 ± 140 BP (GSC-705) and 6150 ± 140 BP (GSC-447) for bison bones collected from outwash in southwestern Alberta. He interpreted the dates as evidence for glacier expansion in the Castle Valley. This interpretation was criticized by Wagner and Eschman (1970) and defended by Stalker (1970); a recent synthesis for the area (Stalker and Harrison 1977) contains no mention of mid-Altithermal glaciation.

Currey (1974) reported a date of 6500 ± 230 BP (GX-3166D) for basal organic sediments in a bog on the inner of two moraine sets at the Temple Lake type locality, Wind River Mountains. If Currey's date is a *close* minimum age, it may indicate a relationship between the Ptarmigan moraine and part, or all, of the type Temple Lake moraine sequence; if, however, it is not a close minimum age, the Temple Lake moraine may be equivalent in its entirety to Satanta Peak or other deposits.

Curry (1970) obtained a date of 7030 ± 130 BP (I-2287) for wood that he believed had been crushed by an advancing rock glacier in the Mammoth Lakes region, Sierra Nevada. He postulated a brief mid-Altithermal period of increased precipitation and glacier growth. Noting that deposits of this age in the Sierra Nevada and Austrian Alps are unusually blocky, he suggested that temperatures had been warm, with frequent fluctuations across the freezing point. There are clear parallels with the situation in the Indian Peaks. However, Curry (1971) later reinterpreted the rock glacier as a landslide deposit, presumably without glacial climatic connotations.

Based on radiocarbon dates from archeological sites in western North America, Benedict (1979a) suggested that the period 7500-5000 BP included two droughts and three intervals of increased winter and spring precipitation, caused by alternating episodes of strong and weak westerly circulation. It is uncertain whether weak westerly airflow, which allows frequent penetration of cold-polar and moist-tropical air masses into the Rocky Mountain foothills and Great Plains, would favor glaciation along the continental divide; the crest of the Front Range can receive significant amounts of winter precipitation from *both* circulation patterns, as illustrated by heavy snowfall during the contrasting winters of 1978-79 and 1979-80. Because of this uncertainty, and because we are dealing with climatic fluctuations so short that they approach or exceed the limits of resolution of present dating methods, it would be premature to correlate the Ptarmigan advance with a specific interval of increased foothills precipitation.

UNDATED ROCK-GLACIER ADVANCE

Two generations of rock glaciers occur along the north-facing walls of most high-altitude Front Range valleys. Although both generations are present in the study area, the older generation is poorly exposed, and not particularly informative. Because of its position in the sequence of deposits, we know that it is intermediate in age between the Ptarmigan moraine and the late Triple Lakes rock-glacier apron. No radiocarbon dates, however, are available; excavations at the Ptarmigan site, beyond the front of the rock glacier, failed to produce sediments related to its advance. B-horizon development and absence of internal ice suggest that the rock glacier may pre-date other rock glaciers in the study area by a substantial amount; however, such relative-age criteria are not considered to be reliable when dealing with rock glaciers.

ALTITHERMAL SOIL FORMATION

Differences between post-Pinedale, post-Satanta Peak, and post-Ptarmigan soils in the study area are minor (Fig. 9). Much of the oxidation encountered in deposits of these ages is likely to have occurred during the latter part of the Altithermal, when temperatures were high, snowbanks were smaller than they are today, and frost processes were greatly reduced in intensity. Late Altithermal A1 horizons have been identified at five localities in the Indian Peaks (Burns 1979; Benedict 1979c, this paper; Benedict and Olson 1978). At three they were preserved *in situ*, or slightly modified by frost action; at two, soil humus had been eroded and redeposited. Radiocarbon dates cluster within a few centuries of 5600 BP, the mean of 9 individual age determinations.

At profile locality 5 in the Fourth of July valley study area, redeposited humus in loess above Satanta Peak outwash (Fig. 29) is believed to have eroded from a late Altithermal soil. A radiocarbon date of 5910 ± 115 BP (I-11,370A) applies to formation of the soil from which the humus was eroded. The date is a maximum age for deposition of the loess, exceeding its true age by the mean residence time of organic carbon in the A1 horizon at time of erosion.

A weakly-developed A1b horizon in a ridge of disturbed lake and outwash sediments at the front of a late Triple Lakes lobate rock glacier also may date from the late Altithermal. The A horizon did not contain sufficient organic matter for a radiocarbon date; however, an associated projectile point (Fig. 44) resembles a style found in small numbers at sites of the Mount Albion complex (Benedict and Olson 1978); seven radiocarbon dates for the complex range from 5800 ± 125 BP (I-3267) to 5350 ± 130 BP (I-4419).

EARLY TRIPLE LAKES ADVANCES

An important objective of the study was to obtain independent evidence that would confirm or refute previous age estimates for deposits at the Triple Lakes type locality in Arapaho Cirque (Benedict 1973a). This was only partially successful. No deposits of *early* Triple Lakes age (*ca.* 5000-4000 yr BP) could be proven to exist in the Fourth of July valley study area, although the oldest generation of rock glaciers — not yet radiocarbon dated — may have developed during this time period.

The older of two loess units at profile locality 5 (Fig. 29) accumulated between 5910 ± 115 BP (I-11,370A) and 3385 ± 95 BP (I-11,134), and may relate to the interval in question. It is tempting to describe it as an early Triple Lakes loess, derived from active valley-train deposits in the vicinity or from erosion of upland areas by frost processes. However, this is conjectural, and does not prove that a glacial advance was in progress. Evidence for patterned-ground reactivation in the study area during early Triple Lakes time is equally equivocal.

LATE TRIPLE LAKES ADVANCE

Late Triple Lakes rock glaciers are well represented in the Fourth of July valley study area. Like a rock glacier at the Triple Lakes type locality in Arapaho Cirque (dated at *ca.* 3000 ^{14}C yr BP by Benedict [1973a]), the deposits are blocky and unstable, with steep fronts that indicate surviving internal ice. Soil-profile development is weak. Maximum *R. geographicum* s.l. diameters range from 90 to 116 mm.

Several limiting ages were obtained during the present study. The most useful and precise are from the Fourth of July Valley Bog, where clastic sediments recording the arrival and initial activity of a rock glacier are bracketed by radiocarbon dates of 3340 ± 65 BP (I-11,091 avg.) and 2970 ± 65 BP (I-11,090 avg.). The base of the clastic layer is sharply defined, suggesting that advance to the edge of the bog was rapid, if not catastrophic. The rock glacier is stationary, or nearly so, at present.

Glaciers or rock glaciers may also have been active at the *head* of the valley during late Triple Lakes time, judging from a date of 2910 ± 65 BP (average of I-5452 and I-5453) for basal peat above outwash sediments near the stream in the Fourth of July Valley Bog. A period of rock-glacier activity near Sawtooth Peak, 14 km to the north, concluded shortly before 2855 ± 90 BP (I-7461, Benedict 1979c).

Although it seems certain that an important rock-glacier advance was underway in the Indian Peaks between 3300 and 3000 BP, it is less certain that this was a time of severe glacial climate. Conceivably, rock glaciers that had formed during an earlier climatic interval could have advanced to their modern positions at a time when warm summer temperatures encouraged deformation of interstitial or buried massive ice. It would be premature, with present limited knowledge of rock-glacier origin and flow, to infer a specific set of climatic conditions for late Triple Lakes time.

AUDUBON ADVANCES

Moraines and rock glaciers did not develop in the Fourth of July valley study area during Audubon time. However, there is evidence for snowbank expansion, and for three episodes of rock-glacier reactivation. Widespread destruction of lichen communities on the floor of the valley indicates that 90-95% of the study area remained snowcovered until mid or late summer for at least a few years during this period. Vascular plants requiring long growing seasons must have been virtually eliminated from the study area, allowing greatly accelerated soil erosion such as is inferred to have occurred at site 5 BL 120. The ages of the oldest lichens to recolonize the devastated area range from 1900 to 1600 ^{14}C years; snowbanks persisted longer in topographic lows, and in protected areas such as site 5 BL 170, where lichen recolonization was delayed for additional centuries.

Evidence for Audubon snowbank expansion has been found at a number of other localities in the Front Range (Benedict 1973*a*, 1975*b*, 1979*b*, Carroll 1974), and Medicine Bow Mountains (Oviatt 1977). It is uncertain how far beyond the limits of the Southern Rockies this event should be recognizable; judging from present snowmelt patterns (for example, see Fig. 31) and the preliminary results of an experimental study of lichen mortality, the change in climate need not have been dramatic.

Moraines of Audubon age in Front Range cirques are few and small. Development of a persistent snowcover in timberline valleys at a time when glacial activity in the cirques was minor suggests that summers were cool, and winters snowy, but that wind-drift concentration of snow was less important than at present. One or more episodes of heavy winter precipitation and low summer temperature, lasting just long enough to kill the lichen cover, but not long enough to cause major changes in glacier mass balance, are the most probable explanation. Interestingly, no comparable destruction of lichen communities occurred during the 17th, 18th, or 19th centuries, when glaciers at least as extensive as those of Audubon time were present in many Front Range cirques.

Layers of sand and silt in the Fourth of July Valley Bog indicate that a rock glacier at the south edge of the bog was reactivated, or that late-lying snow encouraged erosion of its front, on two occasions between 2455 ± 60 BP (I-11,080 avg.) and 1585 ± 55 BP (I-11,079 avg.). These correspond to the principal period(s) of snowbank expansion identified lichenometrically in the study area. A brief interval of stabilization, during which clastic sediments were no longer shed by the rock-glacier front, is dated at about 1845 ± 55 BP (I-11,337 avg.). A final episode of rock-glacier reactivation, which contributed minor amounts of silt and sand to the floor of the bog, is estimated to have occurred between about 1200 and 900 BP, based on extrapolated sedimentation rates; the latter are rough estimates, of low reliability.

It is clear, from these data, that Audubon snowbank expansion began earlier in the Indian Peaks timberline region than was previously supposed (Benedict 1968, 1973*a*). A revised age estimate for the Audubon advance is 2400 to 900 radiocarbon years. This estimate is based upon radiocarbon dates for clastic sediments in the Fourth of July Valley and Caribou Lake Bogs, lichenometric dates for moraine stabilization in Front Range cirques (Benedict 1968), radiocarbon dates for buried late-Audubon glacial ice in Arapaho Cirque (Benedict 1973*b*), and radiocarbon dates for an episode of accelerated downslope soil movement above timberline on Niwot Ridge (Benedict 1966).

ARAPAHO PEAK ADVANCES

No glaciers or rock glaciers developed in the Fourth of July valley study area during Arapaho Peak time (*ca.* 350-100 BP), although glaciers were advancing spectacularly in other parts of the world (Porter and Denton 1967). Snowfall was apparently inadequate to nourish glacier growth along north-facing cliffs in the study area, which are unfavorably oriented for wind-drifting. Glacial activity in the Indian Peaks was confined to cirques in which redistribution of snow by wind and avalanching was important. The best example is Arapaho Cirque, which faces east-southeast and receives 2.6 to 3.9 times the amount of snowfall that would accumulate if it were not for such redistribution processes (J. Johnson 1979): here well-defined moraines record three glacial advances during Arapaho Peak time (Benedict 1973*a*).

No general expansion of snowcover comparable to that of Audubon time affected the study area during the Arapaho Peak advances. This is in contrast to north-central Baffin Island, where "lichen-free" areas surrounding modern icefields and snowbanks suggest a 35% increase in general snow and ice cover between 350 and 100 yr BP (Locke and Locke 1977).

CONCLUSIONS

(1) There is no obvious pattern to the record of Front Range cirque glaciation during the past 12,000 yr, and therefore no basis for predicting future climatic change. The apparent absence of cyclicity may indicate that the glacial advances of post-Pinedale time were triggered by random mechanisms or aperiodic events. The relationship of Front Range glaciers to volcanic eruptions is a promising direction for future research.

(2) The Front Range chronology agrees poorly with the pattern of worldwide Holocene glacier fluctuations hypothesized by Denton and Karlén (1973, Fig. 1). Without better-dated local sequences than currently exist, fundamental questions concerning global synchroneity (Grove 1979) cannot be satisfactorily answered.

(3) The concept of Neoglaciation, as conceived by Porter and Denton (1967) and elaborated by Denton and Porter (1970), is difficult to apply to the Front Range, where small glaciers advanced repeatedly during post-Pinedale time. Advances were similar in frequency, although not in timing, to those reported by Patzelt and Bortenschlager

(1973) and Schneebeli and Rothlisberger (1976) in the Austrian and Swiss Alps, where Heuberger (1974) has also criticized the concept of Neoglaciation.

(4) The sequence of moraines and rock glaciers in high Front Range valleys is unusually detailed because successive ice advances tended to become smaller with time, and to shift from north-facing to east-facing orientations. Without such changes, the morainal record of early postglacial time would probably have been destroyed, giving the false impression of glacier resurgence during Neoglaciation.

(5) Just as the concept of Neoglaciation is not supported by the Front Range glacial chronology, neither are the modified Blytt-Sernander climatic episodes advocated by Baerreis and Bryson (1965) and Bryson et al. (1970), and used as a climatic framework by many Plains archeologists. Nor does there appear to be local geologic significance to the chronostratigraphic subdivisions of postglacial time proposed by Scandinavian workers (Mangerud et al. 1974).

Appendix A

PRINCIPAL ROCK TYPES IN EXCAVATED CHIPPING DEBRIS FROM SITE 5 BL 120

FINE-GRAINED WHITE ORTHOQUARTZITE (N=1053)

White (N8/) orthoquartzite, rarely light yellowish brown (10YR 6/4) to dark yellowish brown (10YR 4/4). Several flakes are banded white and yellowish brown. The quartzite is composed of well-sorted, very fine to fine (0.05-0.20 mm) quartz sand grains in an inconspicuous matrix of clear silica. Widely scattered very fine black heavy-mineral particles are present. Heating experiments show that white flakes experience no color change, or become gray (10YR 5/1) or (rarely) reddish yellow (5YR 6/6) when burned; yellowish brown flakes become weak red (10R 4/3) or dusky red (10R 3/3). The quartzite fractures evenly, across individual grains, and can be flaked with a high degree of precision. All of the projectile points from the site, and many other chipped-stone tools, are made of this rock type.

MEDIUM-GRAINED LIGHT BROWN TO LIGHT REDDISH BROWN ORTHOQUARTZITE (N=11)

Light brown (7.5YR 6/4) to light reddish brown (5YR 6/4) medium-grained orthoquartzite. Composed of interlocking grains of fine to medium coarse sand (0.1-0.5 mm), whose broken faces give flake surfaces an adamantine luster. No matrix is visible. Widely-scattered heavy-mineral grains are present. This rock type is not significantly different from the preceding, and could have been quarried from a coarse-textured facies of the same formation.

BROWN TO REDDISH BROWN QUARTZITE WITH PROMINENT CHERT MATRIX (N=24)

Flakes of this rock type consist of well-sorted, rounded to subrounded, very fine to medium-grained (0.05-0.40 mm) quartz sand grains, set in a prominent matrix of milky white chert. Sand-grain surfaces are stained brown (10YR 5/3) to reddish brown (2.5YR 5/4), giving the quartzite a pepper-and-salt appearance. The matrix accounts for an estimated 20% of the whole rock. Detrital glauconite granules are present in one flake, suggesting a marine origin and possible Cambrian age for the quartzite. The green color of the glauconite shows that it has not been oxidized (Pettijohn 1957: 149), and indicates that the red-

dish brown color of the flake is original (due to coatings of hematite) rather than a result of burning at the site.

PURPLISH PINK CHERT (N=32)

Coarsely-banded light to dark purplish pink chert (not in *Munsell Soil Color Charts*), with a dull to shiny luster. Opaque. Homogeneous except for widely-scattered subangular to subrounded detrital quartz sand grains, less than 0.2 mm in diameter, and rare vugs and veinlets filled with milky white chalcedony and microcrystalline quartz.

PALE BROWN CHERT CONGLOMERATE (N=22)

This rock type consists of subangular to rounded pebbles of chert in a matrix of finely granulated chert and clear chalcedony. Chert pebbles are variable in size and color, with shades of very pale brown (10YR 8/4), pale brown (10YR 6/3), and yellow (10YR 8/6) predominating. The chert is opaque, very finely floccular, and has a slightly shiny luster. Black impurities are locally present in the chalcedony matrix; a stylolitic suture, stained red by iron oxide, traverses a tool made of this material.

DULL BROWN CHERT (N=14)

Brown (10YR 5/3) chert. Slightly translucent, with a dull luster. Homogeneous except for widely-scattered inclusions of microcrystalline quartz, 0.2-0.4 mm in diameter. When heated, this rock type oxidizes dusky red (2.5YR 3/3), but retains its dull luster.

FOSSILIFEROUS BROWN CHERT WITH BLACK DENDRITIC INCLUSIONS (N=12)

Opaque brown (7.5YR 5/4-5/5) fossiliferous chert containing prominent, widely-spaced, black dendritic inclusions that weather white on exposure to the elements. Fossil fragments have sub-parallel preferred orientations. They include a biserial foram (cf. *Textularia*), a fusalinid, a crinoid, and a bryozoan (cf. *Rhombopera*, indicating a Pennsylvanian age (John Chronic, pers. comm. 1980). The chert has a dull to slightly shiny luster, and oxidizes dark red (2.5YR 3/6) when heated. This was the second most common rock type in tools from the site.

DARK YELLOWISH BROWN CHALCEDONY (N=12)

Dark yellowish brown (10YR 4/6) chalcedony. Dull luster. The overall cloudy appearance of the chalcedony is due to very fine, clay-sized particulates. Tiny veinlets of clearer material also occur. Translucent. Oxidizes dusky red (10R 3/4) upon heating.

CLEAR TO BROWNISH YELLOW CHERT/CHALCEDONY WITH DETRITAL QUARTZ SAND GRAINS (N=8)

Clear chalcedony containing diffuse translucent inclusions of brownish yellow (10YR 6/6) chert. Some flakes contain black dendrites. However, the principal distinguishing characteristic of this rock type is the presence of abundant (ca. 10% by volume) rounded to subrounded very fine to medium detrital quartz sand grains, whose broken surfaces sparkle, in contrast to the dull chalcedony matrix in which they are embedded. Heating causes oxidation of the yellow chert to a weak red (10R 4/3) color.

DARK RED "SNOWFLAKE" CHALCEDONY (N=8)

Translucent dark red (2.5YR 3/5) chalcedony, containing fine (0.1-0.5 mm), evenly-spaced, spherical black dendritic inclusions that weather to a white "snowflake" pattern on exposed flake surfaces. One of the flakes includes the wall of a cavity lined with botryoidal chalcedony. Part of another flake is brecciated. Dull to slightly shiny luster. No change in color was observed in heating experiments.

GRAY TO WHITE CHERT/CHALCEDONY (N=3)

Translucent light gray (10YR 7/2) to white (N 8/) chalcedony, containing clouds and diffuse spherical inclusions of opaque white chert as large as 3 mm. Dull luster. Heating produces no color change. An edge-retouched flake knife from the site is made of this rock type.

Appendix B

TYPE DESCRIPTIONS OF PROJECTILE POINTS

PRYOR STEMMED

Pryor Stemmed points are named for their occurrence in Bottleneck Cave (48 BH 206), at the east end of the Pryor Mountains, northern Wyoming (Husted 1969). The points were characteristic of Occupation III, dated at 8040 ± 220 BP (SI-241) and 8160 ± 180 BP (SI-240). The type description is based on 13 specimens.

Husted (1969: 51-52) describes the points as "medium to large stemmed projectile points with alternately beveled edges. Lateral edges vary from parallel to convex and are alternately beveled with the bevel on the right (tip up). Beveling extends at least from the tip to the shoulder, and on some specimens extends the full length of the stem.

Serration of lateral edges ranges from fine and even through rough and irregular to nearly nonexistent. Serrations were made on the beveled edge; the amount of beveling and the quality of the material used determined the fineness of the serrations.

"Stems vary in length from one-fifth to one-third the total length of the points. Edges range from concave through parallel to contracting, and bases are shallowly concave. The lateral and basal edges are ground smooth.

"Shoulders range from straight and prominent through sloping to nearly lacking. In the latter instance, shoulders are represented by a slight angle between the stem and the blade portion.

"Chipping varies from crude parallel-oblique to random, and the quality of the flaking is fair to good. Edges are retouched only on the beveled edge. Basal edges are thinned but wedge-like in appearance. Specimens with slight to moderate beveling are lenticular in cross section. Those with pronounced beveling are rhomboidal. Material: chert (seven), quartzite (six). Lengths: 72 to 52 mm., widths: 20 to 17 mm., thicknesses: 8 to 6 mm." (Husted 1969: 51-52, Fig. 23).

Frison and Grey (1980) discuss the distribution of Pryor Stemmed points in Wyoming and Montana, emphasizing the mountain-foothills orientation of their users, and illustrating specimens from a number of sites.

JAMES ALLEN

James Allen points were named by Mulloy (1959) for the discoverer of the James Allen site, a bison kill at the southern edge of the Laramie Basin, Wyoming, 120 km due north of the Fourth of July valley. The type description is based on 30 more-or-less fragmentary points. A radiocarbon date on burned bison bone was 7900 ± 400 BP (M-304, Crane and Griffin 1958: 1102).

According to Mulloy (1959: 114), "Allen points demonstrate an extremely narrow range of variation in shape and flaking technique. The shape is lanceolate without notches. The edges incurve to a rather rounded point, tend to be parallel at the midsection, and very slightly incurve toward the base, sometimes expanding to a suggestion of a fishtail base. This occasionally produces a scarcely perceptible constriction of the proximal third of the point which is frequently slightly more apparent on one side than the other. This constriction seems to be more a function of the smooth grinding of the proximal third of the edges than of a contour deliberately produced by pressure flaking.

"Bases have rounded corners and are indented to a distance usually about one-quarter of the basal width. Central thinning of the base was accomplished by the removal of one or more longitudinal flakes and usually extended about one-half the width of the base. The basal concavity was ground smooth. Cross sections are uniformly lenticular with thin, sharp, and regular edges. There is a tendency for small chips to break off the edges on the distal third of the point .

"The most distinctive feature of these points is the excellent oblique, parallel flaking. The uniformity of the flaking and the length of the flakes both reflect a skill in pressure flaking far out of the ordinary. The flake scars cross the surface of the blade at an angle which varies from transverse to about 60° with the longitudinal" (Mulloy 1959: 114).

Twenty five of the points were quartzite, one was metamorphosed siltstone, and the remainder cryptocrystalline. The largest point in the collection was estimated, from a fragmentary specimen, to have been approximately 114 mm long, 28 mm wide, and 4.8 mm thick. The smallest in "the normal range of size variation" was a resharpened point 3.25 inches (83 mm) long [probably an error for 2.25 inches (57 mm)], 26 mm wide, and 5.6 mm thick.

Related styles are the Frederick point, which has a shallower basal concavity (Irwin-Williams et al. 1973: 50); the Lusk point, which is less well-flaked and proportionately narrower (Irwin-Williams et al. 1973: 51); and the Angostura point, also relatively narrow, with a shallowly concave to straight base (Agogino et al. 1964: 1351-52). All have lanceolate form and parallel-oblique flaking, and are related closely in time and space. Frison (1978: 37) considers these, and certain other parallel-oblique-flaked points to be "local or regional variants of the terminal Paleo-Indian manifestation for the Northwestern Plains".

McKEAN LANCEOLATE

McKean Lanceolate points were named for their occurrence at three stratified campsites on the McKean ranch, Keyhole Reservoir area, Wyoming. The sites were the Belle Rockshelter (48 CK 4), the Mule Creek Rockshelter (48 CK 204), and the McKean site (48 CK 7), the latter excavated by Mulloy (1954). The type description (Wheeler 1952: 40-41) is based on 28 specimens, most of them fragmentary. Solid-carbon dates for the rockshelters (Libby 1952) are clearly too young; the point style is dated elsewhere at about 5000-3000 radiocarbon years BP.

The point is lanceolate, but with considerable variation in outline. "The base has a deep, usually symmetrical notch, 3.5 to 7 mm deep and approximately 6 to 10 mm wide; or less commonly, a shallow, usually symmetrical notch 1.5 to 2.5 mm deep and approximately 4.5 to 9 mm wide" (Wheeler 1952: 40).

In cross section and longitudinal section the points are generally lenticular, rarely plano-convex. The blade shows moderately well-controlled pressure flaking. "Usually both faces of the blade are fully flaked; but in 5 cases (out of 28), one face of the blade is fully flaked and the opposite face is retouched along the edges only. In every instance the edges of the blade are thin, slightly sinuous, and somewhat uneven. There is no evidence of edge-smoothing or grinding.

"The basal notch was apparently produced by removing one flake or several flakes from each face in the direction of the tip. The lateral projections are usually thinned bifacially and are rounded, pointed, or irregular in outline; they are rarely of the same length and breadth. The edge of the notch is thin and sharp" (Wheeler 1952: 41).

Most points in the type collection were made of fine-grained quartzite, with chert, chalcedony, and jasper also represented. Lengths: 60 to 33 mm, widths 20 to 14 mm, thicknesses 6 to 3 mm.

Additional data on projectile points from the McKean site, including a photograph of 17 representative specimens, is provided by Green (1975).

DUNCAN

The Duncan point is a stemmed variant of the McKean Lanceolate point, and was considered by Mulloy (1954: 27) to represent one end member in a continuous series of variation. Wheeler's (1954) type description is based on points from the Keyhole Reservoir area, Wyoming, and the Angostura Reservoir area, South Dakota.

According to Wheeler (1954: 7), "The Duncan point is a chipped stone projectile point characterized by a straight converging or bilaterally convex blade; insloping, non-barbed shoulders; and a straight parallel-sided or slightly expanding stem with shallowly notched base ... the stem represents about one-fourth of the total length ... the blade and stem are fully chipped by pressure on both faces from the edges in a random fashion. The blade is lenticular in cross section. The base is notched by pressure chipping on both faces from the base toward the tip. The edges of the blade are generally thin, straight, even, and sharp. The sides of the stem are usually smoothed by retouching or grinding". All five specimens illustrated by Wheeler (1954, Fig. 1 *a-e*) are made of quartzite. They have the following dimensions: length, 46 to 32 mm; width, 22 to 16 mm; thickness, 8.5 to 4.2 mm.

Appendix C

PRINCIPAL ROCK TYPES IN CHIPPING DEBRIS FROM SITE 5 BL 170

1. DULL PINK-RED CHERT (N=96)

Uniformly-colored weak red (10R 4/4-5/4) chert. Opaque, with a dull luster, interrupted by the vitreous sparkle of widely-scattered fine to medium (less than 0.4 mm) quartz sand grains. Massive, without veins or inclusions. The source of this rock type is unknown.

2. FLOCCULAR YELLOWISH BROWN CHERT IN CHALCEDONY MATRIX (N=100)

Fine floccules of opaque dark yellowish brown (10YR 4/4-4/6) to yellowish brown (10YR 5/4) chert in a matrix of clear to milky white chalcedony. This rock type appears to have hardened from a colloidal gel, although there are no veinlets of chalcedony to indicate shrinkage during dehydration. Burned flakes are oxidized dark red (2.5YR 3/6) to dark reddish brown (2.5YR 2/4); considerable color variation can occur within individual flakes. Luster varies from dull to shiny, perhaps as a result of differing thermal histories. The source of this rock type, which is common in collections from the Indian Peaks, is unknown.

3. GRAY TO WHITE CHERT/CHALCEDONY (N=480)

The most common rock type in the flake collection is a translucent grayish brown (10YR 5/2) to white chert or chalcedony, with opaque spherical inclusions of white chert, the latter accounting for 1-5% of the rock. Inclusions are 5 mm or less in diameter; most are smaller than 1 mm. A few of the larger inclusions grade inward into microcrystalline quartz. There are no veins or vugs. A dull luster is characteristic, although a few of the flakes are shiny. The nearest known outcrop of this rock type is near Kremmling, in Middle Park, Colorado. A small triangular biface and the base of a corner-notched projectile point from the site are made of this material.

4. FIBROUS DARK YELLOWISH BROWN SILICIFIED WOOD (N=52)

Unburned flakes of this rock type consist of fine, parallel, dark yellowish brown (10YR 4/4) to olive brown (2.5Y 4/4) chert filaments in a matrix of clear chalcedony or white chert. The filaments are circular in cross section; there are approximately 20 per millimeter of flake surface, giving the rock a fibrous appearance. In addition to this primary lineation, visible in hand sample, there is a very fine transverse lineation that is visible microscopically. Damage to the wood prior to silicification is indicated by local areas of crushing, and by irregular fractures filled with clear chalcedony. Voids in the larger fractures are lined with crystalline quartz. The flakes are opaque, except for veinlets of chalcedony, and have a dull to resinous luster. Burned flakes are oxidized dusky red (2.5YR 3/2) to black (10YR 2/1). The source of the silicified wood is unknown. A tool fragment and the base of a corner-notched projectile point, both badly burned, were made of this material.

5. LIGHT GRAY TO YELLOWISH BROWN ORTHO-QUARTZITE (N=36)

Light gray (10YR 7/1) to grayish brown (2.5Y 5/3) even-grained orthoquartzite, grading to yellowish brown (10YR 5/4). The rock is composed of tightly-packed, rounded to subrounded, fine (0.1-0.3 mm) quartz sand grains in a minor chalcedony matrix, the latter visible only where altered by surficial weathering. The quartzite fractures across individual grains, rather than along grain boundaries. Burning causes oxidation to a reddish brown (2.5YR 5/4) or dusky red (10R 3/4) color. Part of the worn exterior surface of a stream cobble is preserved on one flake, suggesting that the quartzite is derived from terrace gravels. Similar quartzites occur in terrace deposits both east and west of the Front Range. A triangular biface and the bases of two corner-notched projectile points from the site are made of this rock type.

6. OLIVE BROWN CHERT WITH DRUSE QUARTZ INCRUSTATIONS (N=46)

Light olive brown (2.5Y 5/4) to olive brown (2.5Y 4/4) chert, irregularly criss-crossed by veins of clear to milky chalcedony. Some of the veins contain geode-like voids, lined with quartz crystals. Others are stained dark by unidentified impurities. The rock has an irregular fracture, revealing internal surfaces that are finely coated with druse quartz; these surfaces are younger than the veins of chalcedony that they transect. Burning alters the chert to a dark red (10R 3/6) color, grading to dark reddish brown (5YR 3/2), but does not change its luster, which remains dull to slightly shiny. The chert is slightly translucent; burning causes it to become opaque.

7. PINK (WEAK RED) CHALCEDONY WITH BLACK DENDRITIC INCLUSIONS (N=22)

Weak red (10R 5/3) chalcedony, shiny and translucent except for rare dull pinkish white inclusions, which occur in less than 10% of the flakes. All of the flakes contain sparse, fine, black, diffusely-spherical dendritic inclusions. This is a very high-quality rock type; its source is unknown.

8. LIGHT GRAY AND WHITE SILICIFIED WOOD (N=50)

The rock is coarsely banded light gray (10YR 6/1) and white, the gray bands consisting of finely cross-laminated to massive opaque chert, and the white bands consisting of single or double columns of cells, each cell having a center of chalcedony and a wall of opaque white chert. The wood is opaque, normally with a dull luster. Burned (or heat-treated) pieces are streaked dusky red (10R 3/4) and have a shiny luster. A side-notched projectile point from the site is made of this rock type, the source of which is unknown.

9. BROWN, DENDRITIC, STYLOLITIC CHERT (N=85)

Translucent brown (10YR 5/3 to 7.5YR 5/3) chert or chalcedony, finely speckled with dark gray (10YR 4/1), very dark gray (10YR 3/1), or black (10YR 2/1) inclusions, arranged in dense, diffuse clusters. Burning causes oxidation of the chalcedony matrix to a yellowish brown (10YR 5/6) or dark reddish brown (2.5YR 5/6) color. An identifying characteristic of this rock type is the presence, in most flakes, of fine stylolitic sutures, with a relief of 0.1-0.5 mm. The sutures are emphasized by an accumulation of insoluble residues, commonly reddish brown in color, and by the fact that the flake surface is generally higher on one side of the suture than on the other. Flakes of this rock type tend to have roughened surfaces and dull lusters. The chert is very distinctive, but has not yet been traced to its source.

10. PINK TO WHITE CHERT BRECCIA IN RED MATRIX (N=25)

This rock type consists of small (less than 0.5 mm), granulated, angular fragments of pink to white chert, set in a dark red (10R 3/6) or dusky red (10R 3/3-3/4) spiderweb matrix. Chert clasts show no preferred orientation. The rock is generally opaque, with a dull luster. Several flakes show a transition into massive, very slightly translucent, dusky red (10R 3/4) chert with a shiny luster.

11. VERY DARK BROWN AND WHITE SILICIFIED WOOD (N=13)

Very dark brown (10YR 2/3) silicified wood, finely laminated, without visible cell structure. Slightly translucent. Dull to shiny luster. The wood is broken into irregularly-angular blocks, which are bounded by veinlets

126

of clear to milky white chalcedony. Many
flakes contain vugs, filled with milky white
chalcedony and grading inward into microcrystalline quartz.

12. BLOCKS OF VERY DARK BROWN SILICIFIED WOOD IN A MATRIX OF YELLOWISH BROWN CHERT (N=20)

The principal constituent of this distinctive
rock type, accounting for 60-70% of exposed
flake surfaces, is a dull, opaque, yellowish
brown (10YR 5/5-5/6) massive chert, containing discontinuous thin (less than 0.2 mm),
randomly-oriented chalcedony veinlets, probably representing shrinkage cracks. Within
this cherty matrix occur blocks of coarse-
grained silicified wood. These are a centimeter or more in maximum dimension, with ragged
boundaries, and with halos of massive, dark
yellowish brown (10YR 4/8) chert. Each block
of wood consists of alternating laminae of
dark yellowish brown (10YR 4/8) opaque chert
and very dark brown (10YR 2/2) translucent
chalcedony, the latter responsible for the
overall dark color of the silicified wood.
Cell structure is not preserved. This is the
only important rock type, other than white
chert/chalcedony, that occurs in the southern
sector of the excavation area. Decortication
flakes suggest that at least one tool was
manufactured at the site from this material.
The wood may be from the trunk of a palm tree
(John Chronic, pers. comm. 1980). It can be
duplicated in the Denver Formation (early
Tertiary) near Parker, Colorado, and probably
elsewhere in the Denver Basin.

References

Agogino, G.A., Rovner, I., and Irwin-Williams, C., 1964: Early Man in the New World. *Science* 143 (3612): 1350-1352.

Ahler, S.A., 1971: Projectile point form and function at Rodgers Shelter, Missouri. *Missouri Archaeological Society Research Series*, No. 8, 146 pp.

Aikens, C.M., 1970: Hogup Cave. *University of Utah, Anthropological Papers*, No. 93, 212 pp.

Alexander, H.L., Jr., 1963: The Levi site: a Paleo-Indian campsite in central Texas. *American Antiquity* 28 (4): 510-528.

Anderson, L.W., 1978: Late Quaternary chronology of Fourth of July Cirque, Front Range, Colorado. *Geological Society of America, Abstracts with Programs* 10 (5): 209.

Andrews, J.T., 1975: *Glacial Systems: An Approach to Glaciers and their Environments*. Duxbury Press, North Scituate, Mass., 191 pp.

Andrews, J.T. and Barnett, D.M., 1979: Holocene (Neoglacial) moraine and proglacial lake chronology, Barnes Ice Cap, Canada. *Boreas* 8 (3): 341-358.

Andrews, J.T. and Smithson, B.B., 1966: Till fabrics of the cross-valley moraines of north-central Baffin Island, Northwest Territories, Canada. *Geological Society of America Bulletin* 77: 271-290.

Antevs, Ernst, 1948: The Great Basin, with emphasis on Glacial and Postglacial times. III. Climatic changes and pre-white man. *University of Utah Bulletin* 38 (20): 168-191.

Armstrong, J.E., Crandell, D.R., Easterbrook, D.J., and Noble, J.B., 1965: Late Pleistocene stratigraphy and chronology in southwestern British Columbia and northwestern Washington. *Geological Society of America Bulletin* 76: 321-330.

Aschmann, Homer, 1958: Great Basin climates in relation to human occupance. *University of California Archeological Survey Report* 42: 23-40.

Baerreis, D.A. and Bryson, R.A., 1965: Climatic episodes and the dating of the Mississippian cultures. *Wisconsin Archeologist* 46 (4): 203-221.

Barry, R.G., 1973: A climatological transect on the east slope of the Front Range, Colorado. *Arctic and Alpine Research* 5 (2): 89-110.

Barsch, Dietrich, 1977. Nature and importance of mass-wasting by rock glaciers in alpine permafrost environments. *Earth Surface Processes* 2: 231-245.

Baumhoff, M.A. and Heizer, R.F., 1965: Postglacial climate and archaeology in the Desert West. *In* Wright, H.E., Jr. and Frey, D.G. (eds.), *The Quaternary of the United States*. Princeton University Press, pp. 697-707.

Bell, K.L. and Bliss, L.C., 1979: Autecology of *Kobresia bellardii*: why winter snow accumulation limits local distribution. *Ecological Monographs* 49 (4): 377-402.

Benedict, J.B., 1965. Freeze-thaw frequencies and the altitudinal distribution of patterned ground in the Colorado Front Range. Mimeographed report on Geological Society of America Penrose Bequest, 17 pp.

Benedict, J.B., 1966: Radiocarbon dates from a stone-banked terrace in the Colorado Rocky Mountains, U.S.A. *Geografiska Annaler* 48A (1): 24-31.

_____, 1967: Recent glacial history of an alpine area in the Colorado Front Range, U.S.A., I. Establishing a lichen-growth curve. *Journal of Glaciology* 6 (48): 817-832.

_____, 1968: Recent glacial history of an alpine area in the Colorado Front Range, U.S.A., II. Dating the glacial deposits. *Journal of Glaciology* 7 (49): 77-87.

_____, 1970: Downslope soil movement in a Colorado alpine region: rates, processes, and climatic significance. *Arctic and Alpine Research* 2 (3): 165-226.

_____, 1973*a*: Chronology of cirque glaciation, Colorado Front Range. *Quaternary Research* 3 (4): 585-599.

_____, 1973*b*: Origin of rock glaciers. *Journal of Glaciology* 12 (66): 520-522.

_____, 1973*c*: Prehistoric man and environment in the Colorado Front Range: Field work during the summer of 1973. Progress report to the United States Forest Service, 12 pp.

_____, 1974: Early occupation of the Caribou Lake site, Colorado Front Range. *Plains Anthropologist* 19 (63): 1-4.

_____, 1975*a*: The Murray site: a Late Prehistoric game drive system in the Colorado Rocky Mountains. *Plains Anthropologist* 20 (69): 161-174.

_____, 1975*b*: Scratching Deer: a Late Prehistoric campsite in the Green Lakes valley, Colorado. *Plains Anthropologist* 20 (70): 267-278.

_____, 1979*a*: Getting away from it all: a study of man, mountains, and the two-drought Altithermal. *Southwestern Lore* 45 (3): 1-12.

_____, 1979*b*: Excavations at the Blue Lake Valley site, Front Range, Colorado. *Southwestern Lore* 45 (4): 7-17.

_____, 1979*c*: Fossil ice-wedge polygons in the Colorado Front Range: origin and significance. *Geological Society of America Bulletin* 90: 173-180.

Benedict, J.B. and Olson, B.L., 1973: Origin of the McKean Complex: Evidence from timberline. *Plains Anthropologist* 18 (62), parts 1-2, p. 323-327.

_____, 1978: The Mount Albion Complex. A study of prehistoric man and the Altithermal. *Center for Mountain Archeology, Research Report*, No. 1, 213 pp., Ward, Colorado.

Bense, Judy, 1971: Cultural stability on the lower Snake River during the Altithermal. *In* Aikens, C.M. (ed.), *Great Basin Anthropological Conference 1970, Selected Papers*. *University of Oregon Anthropological Papers*, No. 1, p. 37-42.

Berger, R. and Suess, H.E., *eds.*, 1979: *Radiocarbon Dating. Proceedings of the Ninth International Conference, Los Angeles and LaJolla, 1976*. University of California Press, Berkeley, 787 pp.

Beschel, R.E., 1950: Fletchen als Altersmaßstab rezenter Moranen. *Zeitschrift für Gletscherkunde und Glazialgeologie*, N.F., 1: 152-161 (a translation by W. Barr is published in *Arctic and Alpine Research* 5 [4]: 303-309).

_____, 1956: Lichenometrie im Gletschervorfeld. *Jahrb. Ver. Schutze d. Alpenpflanz. -Tiere* 22: 164-185.

_____, 1958*a*: Flechtenvereine der Städte, Stadtflechten und ihr Wachstum. *Berichte des Naturwissenschaftlich-Medizinischen Vereins in Innsbruck* 52: 1-158.

_____, 1958*b*: Lichenometrical studies in West Greenland. *Arctic* 11 (4): 254.

_____, 1961: Dating rock surfaces by lichen growth and its application to glaciology and physiography (lichenometry). *In* Raasch, G.O. (ed.), *Geology of the Arctic*, v. 2, University of Toronto Press, Toronto, p. 1044-1062.

Birkeland, P.W., 1973: Use of relative age-dating methods in a stratigraphic study of rock glacier deposits, Mt. Sopris, Colorado. *Arctic and Alpine Research* 5 (4): 401-416.

Birkeland, P.W., 1974: *Pedology, Weathering, and Geomorphological Research*. Oxford University Press, New York, 285 pp.

Birkeland, P.W. and Shroba, R.R., 1974: The status of the concept of Quaternary soil-forming intervals in the western United States. *In* Mahaney, W.C. (ed.), *Quaternary Environments: Proceedings of a Symposium*. York University, Atkinson College, *Geographical Monographs* 5: 241-276.

Birkeland, P.W., Burke, R.M., and Walker, A.L., 1979a: Variation in chemical parameters of Quaternary soils with time and altitude, Sierra Nevada, California. *Geological Society of America, Abstracts with Programs* 11 (7): 388.

Birkeland, P.W., Colman, S.M., Burke, R.M., Shroba, R.R., and Meierding, T.C., 1979b: Nomenclature of alpine glacial deposits, or, What's in a name? *Geology* 7: 532-536.

Black, R.C., III, 1969: *Island in the Rockies. The History of Grand County, Colorado, to 1930*. Grand County Pioneer Society, 436 pp.

Blackwelder, Eliot, 1931: Pleistocene glaciation in the Sierra Nevada and Basin Range. *Geological Society of America Bulletin* 42: 865-922.

Bonnett, R.B., 1970: Glacial sequence of the upper Boulder Creek drainage basin in the Colorado Front Range. Unpublished Ph.D. Thesis, Geology Department, Ohio State University, 318 pp.

Bray, J.R., 1979: Surface albedo increase following massive Pleistocene explosive eruptions in western North America. *Quaternary Research* 12 (2): 204-211.

Breckenridge, R.M., 1969: Neoglacial geology of Upper Fall Creek Basin, Mummy Range, Colorado. Unpublished M.S. Thesis, Department of Geology, University of Wyoming, 59 pp.

_____, 1974: The use of archaeology in dating Quaternary deposits in the upper Wood River area, Absaroka Range, Wyoming. *In* Wilson, M. (ed.), *Applied Geology and Archaeology: The Holocene History of Wyoming*, Geological Survey of Wyoming, *Reports of Investigations*, No. 10: 22-26.

Brink, J.W., 1977: Frost-heaving and archaeological interpretation. *Western Canadian Journal of Anthropology* 7 (3): 61-73.

Brown, W.H., 1925: A probable fossil glacier. *Journal of Geology* 33: 464-466.

Brumley, J.H., 1975: The Cactus Flower site in southeastern Alberta: 1972-1974 excavations. *National Museums of Canada, National Museum of Man Mercury Series, Archaeological Survey of Canada Paper*, No. 46, 244 pp.

_____, 1978: McKean complex subsistence and hunting strategies in the southern Alberta Plains. *In* Davis, L.B. and Wilson, M. (eds.), *Bison Procurement and Utilization: a Symposium. Plains Anthropologist, Memoir 14*, v. 23, no. 82, pt. 2: 175-193.

Bryan, A.L. and Gruhn, R., 1964: Problems relating to the Neothermal climatic sequence. *American Antiquity* 29 (3): 307-315.

Bryant, Bruce, 1971: Movement measurements on two rock glaciers in the eastern Elk Mountains, Colorado. *U.S. Geological Survey, Professional Paper* 750-B: B108-B116.

Bryson, R.A., Baerreis, D.A., and Wendland, W.M., 1970: The character of late-glacial and post-glacial climatic changes. *In* Dort, W., Jr. and Jones, J.K., Jr. (eds.), *Pleistocene and Recent Environments of the Central Great Plains*. University Press of Kansas, Lawrence, p. 53-74.

Buchner, A.P., 1980: Cultural responses to Altithermal (Atlantic) climate along the eastern margins of the North American grasslands: 5500 to 3000 B.C. *National Museums of Canada, National Museum of Man Mercury Series, Archaeological Survey of Canada Paper*, No. 97, 243 pp.

Buckles, W., 1979: Communication in "Current Research", T.P. Myers (ed.). *American Antiquity* 44 (2): 362.

Buntley, G.J. and Westin, F.C., 1965: A comparative study of developmental color in a Chesnut-Chernozem-Brunizem soil climosequence. *Soil Science Society of America, Proceedings* 29 (5): 579-582.

Burns, S.F., 1979: Buried soils beneath alpine snowbanks may date the end of the Altithermal. *Geological Society of America, Abstracts with Programs* 11 (6): 267-268.

Burrows, C.J. and Orwin, J., 1971: Studies of some glacial moraines in New Zealand — 1. The establishment of lichen-growth curves in the Mount Cook area. *New Zealand Journal of Science* 14 (2): 327-335.

Calkin, P.E. and Ellis, J.M., 1980: A lichenometric dating curve and its application to Holocene glacier studies in the central Brooks Range, Alaska. *Arctic and Alpine Research* 12 (3): 245-264.

Carrara, P.E. and Andrews, J.T., 1973: Problems and applications of lichenometry to geomorphic studies, San Juan Mountains, Colorado. *Arctic and Alpine Research* 5 (4): 373-384.

_____, 1975: Holocene glacial/periglacial record; northern San Juan Mountains, southwestern Colorado. *Zeitschrift für Gletscherkunde und Glazialgeologie* 11 (2): 155-174.

Carroll, Tom, 1974: Relative age dating techniques and a late Quaternary chronology, Arikaree Cirque, Colorado. *Geology* 2 (7): 321-325.

Cegla, Jerzy, 1972: Sedymentacja lessów Polski. *Acta Universitatis Wratislaviensis* 168, *Studia Geograficzne* XVII: 1-72 (extended English summary, p. 64-71).

Colman, S.M., 1976: Inherent factors in the flow of valley glaciers as a possible influence in the formation of stepped glacial valleys. *Zeitschrift für Geomorphologie* N.F., 20 (3): 297-307.

_____, 1977: The development of weathering rinds on basalts and andesites and their use as a Quaternary dating method, western United States. Unpublished Ph.D. Thesis, Department of Geological Sciences, University of Colorado, 235 pp.

Corte, A.E., 1963: Particle sorting by repeated freezing and thawing. *Science* 142 (3591): 499-501.

Crandell, D.R. and Miller, R.D., 1974: Quaternary stratigraphy and extent of glaciation in the Mount Rainier region, Washington. *U.S. Geological Survey, Professional Paper* 847: 1-59.

Crane, H.R., 1956: University of Michigan radiocarbon dates I. *Science* 124: 664-672.

Crane, H.R. and Griffin, J.B., 1958: University of Michigan radiocarbon dates II. *Science* 127: 1098-1105.

Currey, D.R., 1965: An ancient bristlecone pine stand in eastern Nevada. *Ecology* 46 (4): 564-566.

_____, 1974: Probable pre-Neoglacial age of the type Temple Lake moraine, Wyoming. *Arctic and Alpine Research* 6 (3): 293-300.

Curry, R.R., 1969: Holocene climatic and glacial history of the central Sierra Nevada, California. *In* Schumm, S.A. and Bradley, W.C. (eds.), *United States Contributions to Quaternary Research, Geological Society of America Special Paper* 123: 1-47.

_____, 1970: Altithermal precipitation maximum. *Abstracts, First Meeting, American Quaternary Association, Yellowstone Park & Montana State University, Bozeman*: 25.

_____, 1971, Glacial and Pleistocene history of the Mammoth Lakes Sierra, California. *University of Montana, Geological Series, Publication* 11: 1-49.

Davis, P.T. and Waterman, S.E., 1979: New radiocarbon ages for type Triple Lakes moraines, Arapaho Cirque, Colorado Front Range. *Geological Society of America, Abstracts with Programs* 11 (6): 270.

Deevey, E.S., Jr. and Flint, R.F., 1957: Postglacial hypsithermal interval. *Science* 125: 182-184.

DeJong, J.D., 1952: On the structure of the pre-glacial Pleistocene of the Archemerberg (Prov. of Overijsel, Netherlands). *Geologie en Mijnbouw*, ser. 2, v. 14: 86-90.

Denton, G.H. and Karlén, W., 1973: Holocene climatic variations — their pattern and possible cause. *Quaternary Research* 3 (2): 155-205.

_____, 1977: Holocene glacial and tree-line variations in the White River valley and Skolai Pass, Alaska and Yukon Territory. *Quaternary Research* 7 (1): 63-111.

Denton, G.H. and Porter, S.C., 1970: Neoglaciation. *Scientific American* 222 (6): 100-110.

Ellis, Stephen, 1979: Radiocarbon dating evidence for the initiation of solifluction *ca.* 5500 years B.P. at Okstindan, North Norway. *Geografiska Annaler* 61A (1-2): 29-33.

Embleton, C. and King, C.A.M., 1975: *Glacial Geomorphology*. Halsted Press, a Division of John Wiley & Sons, Inc., New York, 573 pp.

Fagan, J.L., 1974: Altithermal occupation of spring sites in the northern Great Basin. *University of Oregon Anthropological Papers* 6: 1-146.

Fleischer, R.L., 1975: Does lightning generate neutrons? *Transactions American Geophysical Union* 56 (6): 368.

Fleischer, R.L., Plumer, J.A., and Crouch, K., 1974: Are neutrons generated by lightning? *Journal Geophysical Research* 79 (33): 5013-5017.

Flint, R.F., 1971: *Glacial and Quaternary Geology*. John Wiley & Sons, Inc., New York, 892 pp.

Follmann, Gerhard, 1961: Lichenometrische Altersbestimmungen an vorchristlichen Steinsetzungen der polynesischen Osterinsel. *Die Naturwissenschaften* 48: 627-628.

_____, 1965: Das Alter der Steinriesen auf der Osterinsel. *Umschau in Wissenschaft und Technik* 12: 374-377.

Fowler, D.D., Madsen, D.B., and Hattori, E.M., 1973: Prehistory of southeastern Nevada. *Desert Research Institute Publications in the Social Sciences* 6: 1-145.

Frison, G.C., 1973: Early Period marginal cultural groups in northern Wyoming. *Plains Anthropologist* 18 (62), pts. 1-2: 300-312.

_____, 1978: *Prehistoric Hunters of the High Plains*. Academic Press, New York, 457 pp.

Frison, G.C. and Grey, D.C., 1980: Pryor Stemmed: a specialized late Paleo-Indian ecological adaptation. *Plains Anthropologist* 25 (87): 27-46.

Fry, E.J., 1927: The mechanical action of crustaceous lichens on substrata of shale, schist, gneiss, limestone, and obsidian. *Annals of Botany* 41 (163): 437-460.

Giddings, J.L., 1963: Some Arctic spear points and their counterparts. *Anthropological Papers of the University of Alaska* 10 (2): 1-12.

_____, 1964: *The Archeology of Cape Denbigh*. Brown University Press, Providence, 331 pp.

Gilet-Blein, N., Marien, G., and Evin, J., 1980: Unreliability of ^{14}C dates from organic matter of soils. *Radiocarbon* 22 (3): 919-929.

Goh, K.M., Molloy, B.P.J., and Rafter, T.A., 1977: Radiocarbon dating of Quaternary loess deposits, Banks Peninsula, Canterbury, New Zealand. *Quaternary Research* 7 (2): 177-196.

Graf, William L., 1971: Quantitative analysis of Pinedale landforms, Beartooth Mountains, Montana and Wyoming. *Arctic and Alpine Research* 3 (3): 253-261.

Green, J.P., 1975: McKean and Little Lake technology: a problem in projectile point typology in the Great Basin of North America. *In* Swanson, E. (ed.), *Lithic Technology. Making and Using Stone Tools*. Mouton & Co., The Hague, p. 159-171.

Greene, A.M., 1968: Age and archaeological association of oblique flaked projectile points at the Betty Greene site, eastern Wyoming. *Abstract of Papers, Thirty-third Annual Meeting of the Society for American Archaeology, Santa Fe*.

Griffey, N.J. and Ellis, S., 1979: Three in situ paleosols beneath Neoglacial moraine ridges, Okstindan and Jotunheimen, Norway. *Arctic and Alpine Research* 11 (2): 203-214.

Griffey, N.J. and Matthews, J.A., 1978: Major Neoglacial glacier expansion episodes in southern Norway: evidences from moraine ridge stratigraphy with ^{14}C dates on buried palaeosols and moss layers. *Geografiska Annaler* 60A: 73-90.

Griffey, N.J. and Whalley, W.B., 1979: A rock glacier and moraine-ridge complex, Lyngen Peninsula, north Norway. *Norsk geogr. Tidsskr.* 33: 117-124.

Grove, J.M., 1979: The glacial history of the Holocene. *Progress in Physical Geography* 3 (1): 1-54.

Gulliksen, Steinar, 1980: Isotopic fractionation of Norwegian materials for radiocarbon dating. *Radiocarbon* 22 (3): 980-986.

Hagar, I.K., 1976: 5 CR 1 — Draper Cave excavation and research report. *Southwestern Lore* 42 (3): 1-13.

Hageman, B.P., 1972: Bulletin 6 from the INQUA Com. Study Holocene, Sept. 1972. 6 pp.

Harden, J.W. and Marchand, D.E., 1977: The soil chronosequence of the Merced River area. *In* Singer, M. J. (ed.), *Soil Development, Geomorphology, and Cenozoic History of the Northeastern San Joaquin Valley and Adjacent Areas, California. Guidebook for Joint Field Session of American Soc. Agron., Soil Sci. Soc. America, and Geological Soc. America*, p. 22-38.

Harkness, D.D. and Burleigh, R., 1974: Possible carbon-14 enrichment in high altitude wood. *Archaeometry* 16: 121-127.

Harris, C. and Ellis, S., 1980: Micromorphology of soils in soliflucted materials, Okstindan, northern Norway. *Geoderma* 23: 11-29.

Hayden, Brian, 1979: Snap, shatter, and superfractures: use-wear of stone skin scrapers. *In* Hayden, B. (ed.), *Lithic Use-wear Analysis*. Academic Press, New York, p. 207-229.

Haynes, C.V., Jr., Damon, P.E., and Grey, D.C., 1966: Arizona radiocarbon dates VI. *Radiocarbon* 8: 1-21.

Haynes, C.V., Jr., Grey, D.C., Damon, P.E., and Bennett, R., 1967: Arizona radiocarbon dates VII. *Radiocarbon* 9: 1-14.

Hays, J.D., Imbrie, J., and Shackleton, N.J., 1976: Variations in the earth's orbit: pacemaker of the ice ages. *Science* 194 (4270): 1123-1131.

Heuberger, Helmut, 1974: Alpine Quaternary glaciation. *In* Ives, J.D. and Barry, R.G. (eds.), *Arctic and Alpine Environments*. Methuen & Co., Ltd., London, p. 319-338.

Hurst, V.J., 1977: Visual estimation of iron in saprolite. *Geological Society of America Bulletin* 88: 174-176.

Hurt, W.R., 1960: A new radiocarbon date from South Dakota. *State University of South Dakota, W.H. Over Museum, Museum News* 21 (11 & 12): 1-3.

_____, 1966: The Altithermal and the prehistory of the Northern Plains. *Quaternaria* 8: 101-114.

Huscher, B.H. and Huscher, H.A., 1941: Continuation of archaeological survey of southern and western Colorado. *Year Book of the American Philosophical Society, 1941*: 226-229.

Husted, W.M., 1965: Early occupation of the Colorado Front Range. *American Antiquity* 30 (4): 494-498.

_____, 1968: Wyoming. *In* Caldwell, W.W., ed., *The Northwestern Plains: A Symposium. Center for Indian Studies, Rocky Mountain College, Occasional Papers* 1: 63-68.

_____, 1969: Bighorn Canyon archeology. *Smithsonian Institution, River Basin Surveys, Publications in Salvage Archeology* 12: 1-138.

_____, 1970: Altithermal occupation of the Northern Rocky Mountains by early plains hunting peoples. *Abstracts, First Meeting, American Quaternary Association, Yellowstone Park & Montana State University, Bozeman*: 69.

_____, 1974: Prehistoric occupation of the alpine zone in the Rocky Mountains. *In* Ives, J.D. and Barry, R.G. (eds.), *Arctic and Alpine Environments*. Methuen & Co., Ltd., London, p. 857-872.

_____, 1978: Excavation techniques and culture layer analyses. *In* McCracken, H. (ed.), *The Mummy Cave Project in Northwestern Wyoming*. The Buffalo Bill Historical Center, Cody (Wyoming), p. 50-132.

Irwin, H.J. and Irwin, C.C., 1959: Excavations at the LoDaisKa site in the Denver, Colorado, area. *Denver Museum of Natural History Proceedings* 8: 1-156.

_____, 1961: Radiocarbon dates from the LoDaisKa site, Colorado. *American Antiquity* 27: 114-115.

Irwin-Williams, C. and Irwin, H.J., 1966: Excavations at Magic Mountain. *Denver Museum of Natural History Proceedings* 12: 1-241.

Irwin-Williams, C., Irwin, H., Agogino, G., and Haynes, C.V., 1973: Hell Gap: Paleo-Indian occupation on the High Plains. *Plains Anthropologist* 18 (59): 40-53.

Ives, R.L., 1942: Early human occupation of the Colorado headwaters region: an archeological reconnaissance. *Geographical Review* 32: 448-462.

_____, 1953: Later Pleistocene glaciation in the Silver Lake Valley, Colorado. *Geographical Review* 43: 229-252.

Jackson, T.A. and Keller, W.D., 1970: A comparative study of the role of lichens and "inorganic" processes in the chemical weathering of recent Hawaiian lava flows. *American Journal of Science* 269: 446-466.

Jennings, J.D., 1957: Danger Cave. *University of Utah Anthropological Papers* 27: 328 pp.

_____, 1964: The Desert West. *In* Jennings, J.D. and Norbeck, E. (eds.), *Prehistoric Man in the New World.* University of Chicago Press, Chicago, p. 149-174.

_____, 1980: Cowboy Cave. *University of Utah Anthropological Papers* 104: 224 pp.

Jennings, J.D., Schroedl, A.R., and Holmer, R.N., 1980: Sudden Shelter. *University of Utah Anthropological Papers* 103: 321 pp.

Johnson, D.L., Muhs, D.R., and Barnhardt, M.L., 1977: The effects of frost heaving on objects in soils, II: laboratory experiments. *Plains Anthropologist* 22 (76), pt. 1: 133-147.

Johnson, J.B., 1979: Mass balance and aspects of the glacier environment, Front Range, Colorado, 1969-1973. Unpublished Ph.D. Thesis, Department of Geological Sciences, University of Colorado, 287 pp.

Kainer, R.E., 1976: Archaeological investigations at the Spring Gulch site (5 LR 252). Unpublished M.A. Thesis, Department of Anthropology, Colorado State University, 227 pp.

Karlén, Wibjörn, 1973: Holocene glacier and climatic variations, Kebnekaise Mountains, Swedish Lapland. *Geografiska Annaler* 55A (1): 29-63.

Katz, P.R., 1971: Archaeology of the Sutter site in northeastern Kansas. *Plains Anthropologist* 16 (51): 1-19.

_____, 1973: Radiocarbon dates from the Sutter site, northeastern Kansas. *Plains Anthropologist* 18 (60): 167-168.

Kiver, E.P., 1972: Two Late Pinedale advances in the southern Medicine Bow Mountains, Colorado. *University of Wyoming, Contributions to Geology* 11 (1): 1-8.

Knox, J.C., 1976: Impact of fluvial erosion on the Great Plains Altithermal cultural hiatus. Paper presented at the symposium "Anthropology on the Great Plains: The State of the Art, 1976". Joint Plains-Midwest Anthropological Conference, Minneapolis, Minnesota, October 20-22, 1976. 48 pp.

Komárková, V., 1979: Alpine vegetation of the Indian Peaks area, Front Range, Colorado Rocky Mountains. *Flora et Vegetatio Mundi* VII. J. Cramer, Vaduz, 591 pp.

Kvamme, K.L., 1977. Aboriginal sandstone quarries in the foothills of northeastern Colorado. *Southwestern Lore* 43 (3): 22-26.

Lahren, L.A., 1976: The Myers-Hindman site: an exploratory study of human occupation patterns in the Upper Yellowstone Valley from 7000 B.C. to A.D. 1200. *Anthropologos Researches International Incorporated.* Livingston, Montana, 195 pp.

Leach, L.L., 1966: Excavations at Willowbrook: a stratified site near Morrison. *Southwestern Lore* 32 (2): 25-46.

Libby, L.M. and Lukens, H.R., 1973: Production of radiocarbon in tree rings by lightning bolts. *Journal of Geophysical Research* 78 (26): 5902-5903.

Libby, W.F., 1952: Chicago radiocarbon dates, III. *Science* 116 (3025): 673-681.

Lindsay, D.C., 1973: Estimates of lichen growth rates in the maritime Antarctic. *Arctic and Alpine Research* 5 (4): 341-346.

Livingstone, D.A. and Clayton, W.D., 1980: An altitudinal cline in tropical African grass floras and its paleoecological significance. *Quaternary Research* 13 (3): 392-402.

Lobdell, J.E., 1973: The Scoggin site: an Early Middle Period Bison kill. *Wyoming Archaeologist* 16 (3): 1-71.

Locke, C.W. and Locke, W.W. III, 1977: Little Ice Age snow-cover extent and paleoglaciation thresholds: north-central Baffin Island, N.W.T., Canada. *Arctic and Alpine Research* 9 (3): 291-300.

Long, A. and Rippeteau, B., 1974: Testing contemporaneity and averaging radiocarbon dates. *American Antiquity* 39 (2), pt. 1: 205-215.

Lovering, T.S. and Goddard, E.N., 1950: Geology and ore deposits of the Front Range, Colorado. *U.S. Geological Survey, Professional Paper* 223: 1-199.

Luckman, B.H., 1977: Lichenometric dating of Holocene moraines at Mount Edith Cavell, Jasper, Alberta. *Canadian Journal of Earth Sciences* 14 (8): 1809-1822.

Mack, R.N., Rutter, N.W., Bryant, V.M., Jr., and Valastro, S., 1978: Reexamination of postglacial vegetation history in northern Idaho: Hager Pond, Bonner Co. *Quaternary Research* 10 (2): 241-255.

Mack, R.N., Rutter, N.W., and Valastro, S., 1979: Holocene vegetation history of the Okanogan Valley, Washington. *Quaternary Research* 12 (2): 212-225.

Madole, R.F., 1969: Pinedale and Bull Lake Glaciation in upper St. Vrain drainage basin, Boulder County, Colorado. *Arctic and Alpine Research* 1 (4): 279-287.

_____, 1976a: Bog stratigraphy, radiocarbon dates, and Pinedale to Holocene glacial history in the Front Range, Colorado. *Journal Research U.S. Geological Survey* 4 (2): 163-169.

_____, 1976b: Glacial geology of the Front Range, Colorado. *In* Mahaney, W.C. (ed.), *Quaternary Stratigraphy of North America*. Dowden, Hutchinson & Ross, Inc., Stroudsburg (Pennsylvania), p. 297-318.

_____, 1980a: Time of Pinedale deglaciation in north-central Colorado: Further considerations. *Geology* 8: 118-122.

_____, 1980b: Glacial Lake Devlin and the chronology of Pinedale Glaciation on the east slope of the Front Range, Colorado. *U.S. Geological Survey, Open-File Report* 80-725: 1-32.

Madsen, D.B. and Currey, D.R., 1979: Late Quaternary glacial and vegetation changes, Little Cottonwood Canyon area, Wasatch Mountains, Utah. *Quaternary Research* 12 (2): 254-270.

Mahaney, W.C., 1973a: Neoglacial chronology in the Fourth of July Cirque, central Colorado Front Range. *Geological Society of America Bulletin* 84: 161-170.

_____, 1973b: Reply. *Geological Society of America Bulletin* 84: 3767-3772.

_____, 1974: Soil stratigraphy and genesis of Neoglacial deposits in the Arapaho and Henderson cirques, central Colorado Front Range. *In* Mahaney, W.C. (ed.), *Quaternary Environments: Proceedings of a Symposium*. York University, Atkinson College, *Geographical Monographs* 5: 197-240.

Maher, L.J., Jr., 1973: Pollen evidence suggests that climatic changes in the Colorado Rockies during the last 5000 years were out of phase with those in the northeastern United States. *Abstracts, Ninth Congress International Union for Quaternary Research, Christchurch, New Zealand*: 227-228.

Mangerud, J., Andersen, S.T., Berglund, B.E., and Donner, J.J., 1974: Quaternary stratigraphy of Norden, a proposal for terminology and classification. *Boreas* 3 (3): 109-128.

Marr, J.W., 1961: Ecosystems of the east slope of the Front Range in Colorado. *University of Colorado Studies, Series in Biology* 8: 1-134.

_____, 1977: The development and movement of tree islands near the upper limit of tree growth in the Southern Rocky Mountains. *Ecology* 58: 1159-1164.

Marr, J.W. and Marr, R.E., 1973: Environment and phenology in the forest-tundra ecotone, Front Range, Colorado. *Arctic and Alpine Research* 5 (3), pt. 2: A65-A66.

Marr, J.W., Clark, J.M., Osburn, W.S., and Paddock, M.W., 1968: Data on mountain environments III. Front Range, Colorado, four climax regions, 1959-1964. *University of Colorado Studies, Series in Biology* 29: 1-181.

Matthews, J.A., 1978: Plant colonisation patterns on a gletschervorfeld, southern Norway: a meso-scale geographical approach to vegetation change and phytometric dating. *Boreas* 7: 155-178.

_____, 1980: Some problems and implications of ^{14}C dates from a podzol buried beneath an end moraine at Haugabreen, southern Norway. *Geografiska Annaler* 62A (3-4): 185-208.

McCracken, H., Wedel, W.R., Edgar, R., Moss, J.H., Wright, H.E., Jr., Husted, W.M., and Mulloy, W., 1978: The Mummy Cave project in northwestern Wyoming. *The Buffalo Bill Historical Center*, Cody, Wyoming, 160 pp.

Mehringer, P.J., Jr., Arno, S.F., and Petersen, K.L., 1977: Postglacial history of Lost Trail Pass Bog, Bitterroot Mountains, Montana. *Arctic and Alpine Research* 9 (4): 345-368.

Mercer, J.H., 1972: The lower boundary of the Holocene. *Quaternary Research* 2 (1): 15-24.

Metcalf, M.D., 1974: Archaeological excavations at Dipper Gap: a stratified butte top site in north-eastern Colorado. Unpublished M.A. Thesis, Department of Anthropology, Colorado State University, 200 pp.

Miller, C.D., 1973: Chronology of Neoglacial deposits in the northern Sawatch Range, Colorado. *Arctic and Alpine Research* 5 (4): 385-400.

_____, 1979: A statistical method for relative-age dating of moraines in the Sawatch Range, Colorado. *Geological Society of America Bulletin*, Part I, v. 90: 1153-1164.

Miller, C.D. and Birkeland, P.W., 1974: Probable pre-Neoglacial age of the type Temple Lake moraine, Wyoming: Discussion and additional relative-age data. *Arctic and Alpine Research* 6 (3): 301-306.

Miller, G.H. and Andrews, J.T., 1972: Quaternary history of northern Cumberland Peninsula, East Baffin Island, N.W.T., Canada. Part VI: Preliminary lichen growth curve. *Geological Society of America Bulletin* 83: 1133-1138.

Miller, T.O., Jr., 1979: Stonework of the Xêtá Indians of Brazil. *In* Hayden, B. (ed.), *Lithic Use-wear Analysis*. Academic Press, New York, p. 401-407.

Millett, M.T., 1956: Glaciation in the headwaters of Middle Boulder Creek, Colorado. Unpublished M.A. Thesis, Department of Geography, University of Colorado, 38 pp.

Mörner, N-A., ed., 1976: The Pleistocene/Holocene boundary: a proposed boundary-stratotype in Gothenburg, Sweden. *Boreas* 5 (4): 193-275.

Mulloy, William, 1954: The McKean site in northeastern Wyoming. *Southwestern Journal of Anthropology* 10 (4): 432-460.

_____, 1958: A preliminary historical outline for the northwestern Plains. *University of Wyoming Publications* 22 (1): 1-235.

_____, 1959: The James Allen site, near Laramie, Wyoming. *American Antiquity* 25 (1): 112-116.

Munsell Color Company, Inc., 1954: *Munsell Soil Color Charts*. Baltimore.

Nance, C.R., 1972: Cultural evidence for the Altithermal in Texas and Mexico. *Southwestern Journal of Anthropology* 28: 169-192.

Nance, J.D., 1971: Functional interpretations from microscopic analysis. *American Antiquity* 36 (3): 361-366.

Nelson, A.R., Millington, A.C., Andrews, J.T., and Nichols, H., 1979: Radiocarbon-dated upper Pleistocene glacial sequence, Fraser Valley, Colorado Front Range. *Geology* 7: 410-414.

Nelson, C.E., 1969: Salvage archaeology on Van Bibber Creek, Site 5 JF 10. *Southwestern Lore* 34 (4): 85-106.

_____, 1971: The George W. Lindsay Ranch site, 5 JF 11. *Southwestern Lore* 37 (1): 1-14.

Nelson, R.L., 1954: Glacial geology of the Frying Pan River drainage, Colorado. *Journal of Geology* 62: 325-343.

Ogden, J.G., III, 1977: The use and abuse of radiocarbon dating. *In* Newman, W.S. and Salwen, B. (eds.) *Amerinds and their Paleoenvironments in Northeastern North America*. *Annals of the New York Academy of Sciences* 288: 167-173.

Olson, E.A. and Broecker, W.S., 1959: Lamont natural radiocarbon measurements V. *Radiocarbon* 1: 1-28.

Olsson, I.U., 1974: Some problems in connection with the evaluation of C^{14} dates. *Geologiska Föreningens i Stockholm Förhandlingar* 96: 311-320.

_____, ed., 1970: *Radiocarbon Variations and Absolute Chronology. Proceedings of the Twelfth Nobel Symposium, Uppsala.* Almqvist & Wiksell Förlag AB, Stockholm, 657 pp.

Osburn, W.S., Jr., 1963: The dynamics of fallout distribution in a Colorado alpine tundra snow accumulation ecosystem. *Radioecology. Proceedings of the First National Symposium on Radioecology, Colorado State University:* 51-71.

_____, 1966: Radioecology of the Colorado Front Range. Terminal Report to U.S. Atomic Energy Commission, Contract No. AT(11-1)-1191. 119 pp.

Østrem, Gunnar, 1965: Problems of dating ice-cored moraines. *Geografiska Annaler* 47A (1): 1-38.

Outcalt, S.I., 1964: Two Ural-type glaciers in Rocky Mountain National Park, Colorado. Unpublished M.A. Thesis, Department of Geography, University of Colorado, 81 pp.

Outcalt, S.I. and Benedict, J.B., 1965: Photointerpretation of two types of rock glacier in the Colorado Front Range, U.S.A. *Journal of Glaciology* 5 (42): 849-856.

Oviatt, C.G., 1977: Glacial geology of the Lake Marie area, Medicine Bow Mountains, Wyoming. *University of Wyoming, Contributions to Geology* 16 (1): 27-38.

Patzelt, G. and Bortenschlager, S., 1973: Die postglazialen Gletscher- und Klimaschwankungen in der Venedigergruppe (Hohe Tauern, Ostalpen). *Zeitschrift für Geomorphologie, N.F., Supplementband* 16: 25-72.

Pearson, R.C. and Johnson, G., 1980: Mineral resources of the Indian Peaks study area, Boulder and Grand Counties, Colorado. *U.S. Geological Survey Bulletin* 1463: 1-109.

Pettijohn, F.J., 1957: *Sedimentary Rocks.* Harper & Brothers, New York, 718 pp.

Pierce, K.L., 1979: History and dynamics of glaciation in the northern Yellowstone National Park area. *U.S. Geological Survey, Professional Paper* 729-F: 1-90.

Porter, S.C., 1975: Weathering rinds as a relative-age criterion: application to subdivision of glacial deposits in the Cascade Range. *Geology* 3 (3): 101-104.

_____, 1978: Glacier Peak tephra in the North Cascade Range, Washington: stratigraphy, distribution, and relationship to late-glacial events. *Quaternary Research* 10 (1): 30-41.

_____, 1981: Lichenometric studies in the Cascade Range of Washington: establishment of a *Rhizocarpon geographicum* growth curve at Mount Rainier. *Arctic and Alpine Research* (in press).

Porter, S.C. and Denton, G.H., 1967: Chronology of Neoglaciation in the North American Cordillera. *American Journal of Science* 265 (3): 177-210.

Price, R.J., 1969: Moraines, sandur, kames and eskers near Breidamerkurjökull, Iceland. *Institute of British Geographers, Transactions* 46: 17-43.

_____, 1970: Moraines at Fjallsjökull, Iceland. *Arctic and Alpine Research* 2 (1): 27-42.

Radnell, C.J., Aitken, M.J., and Otlet, R.L., 1979: In situ ^{14}C production in wood. *In* Berger, R. and Suess, H.E. (eds.), *Radiocarbon Dating, Proceedings of the Ninth International Conference, Los Angeles and La Jolla, 1976.* University of California Press, Berkeley, p. 643-657.

Rafter, T.A. and Grant-Taylor, eds., 1972: *Proceedings of the 8th International Conference on Radiocarbon Dating.* Royal Society of New Zealand, Wellington.

Reeves, Brian, 1973: The concept of an Altithermal cultural hiatus in Northern Plains prehistory. *American Anthropologist* 75 (5): 1221-1253.

Renaud, E.B., 1939: Report on lichen of Spanish Diggings. Work Projects Administration, Work Project No. 885, Quarterly Report, October, November, and December 1939, p. 33.

Richmond, G.M., 1960: Glaciation of the east slope of Rocky Mountain National Park, Colorado. *Geological Society of America Bulletin* 71: 1371-1382.

Richmond, G.M., 1965: Glaciation of the Rocky Mountains. *In* Wright, H.E., Jr. and Frey, D.G. (eds.), *The Quaternary of the United States*. Princeton University Press, Princeton, p. 217-230.

Rutten, M.G., 1960: Ice-pushed ridges, permafrost and drainage. *American Journal of Science* 258: 293-297.

Sanger, David, 1963: Excavations at Nesikep Creek (EdRk:4), a stratified site near Lillooet, British Columbia: preliminary report. *National Museum of Canada, Bulletin* 193, pt. 1: 130-161.

_____, 1966: Excavations in the Lochnore-Nesikep Creek locality, British Columbia: Interim report. *National Museum of Canada, Anthropology Papers* 12: 1-22.

_____, 1967: Prehistory of the Pacific Northwest Plateau as seen from the interior of British Columbia. *American Antiquity* 32 (2): 186-197.

Saul, J.M., 1964: Study of the Spanish Diggings, aboriginal flint quarries of southeastern Wyoming. *National Geographic Society Research Reports:* 183-199.

Schmidt, T.A., 1969: A reconnaissance study of recent glacial and periglacial deposits in a Front Range cirque valley. Typewritten report for Geol. 540, University of Colorado, 24 pp.

Schneebeli, W. and Röthlisberger, F., 1976: 8000 Jahre Walliser Gletschergeschichte. *Die Alpen, Zeitschrift des Schweizer Alpen Club* 52 (3-4): 1-152.

Schumm, S.A., 1977: *The Fluvial System*. John Wiley & Sons, Inc., New York, 338 pp.

Scott, W.E., 1977: Quaternary glaciation and volcanism, Metolius River area, Oregon. *Geological Society of America Bulletin* 88: 113-124.

Sharrock, F.W., 1966: Prehistoric occupation patterns in southwest Wyoming and cultural relationships with the Great Basin and Plains culture areas. *University of Utah Anthropological Papers* 77: 1-215.

Shroba, R.R., 1977: Soil development in Quaternary tills, rock-glacier deposits, and taluses, Southern and Central Rocky Mountains. Unpublished Ph.D. Thesis, Department of Geological Sciences, University of Colorado, 424 pp.

_____, 1978: Soil development in Holocene cirque deposits, Sawatch Range and Front Range, Colorado, and Sangre de Cristo Range, New Mexico. *Geological Society of America, Abstracts with Programs* 10 (5): 238.

Simms, S.R., 1979: High altitude archeology in Utah: a cultural resource inventory of 11 projects and a test excavation (42 SV 1357) in the Fishlake National Forest. *University of Utah, Department of Anthropology, Archeological Center, Reports of Investigations* 79-36: 1-60.

Soil Survey Staff, 1951: *Soil Survey Manual*. U.S. Department of Agriculture, Handbook No. 18. Washington, 503 pp.

_____, 1975: *Soil Taxonomy. A Basic System of Soil Classification for Making and Interpreting Soil Surveys*. U.S. Department of Agriculture, Soil Conservation Service, Agriculture Handbook No. 436. Washington, 754 pp.

Sollberger, J.B., 1971: A technological study of beveled knives. *Plains Anthropologist* 16 (53): 209-218.

Stalker, A. MacS., 1969: A probable late Pinedale terminal moraine in Castle River Valley, Alberta. *Geological Society of America Bulletin* 80 (10): 2115-2122.

_____, 1970: A probable late Pinedale terminal moraine in Castle River Valley, Alberta: Reply. *Geological Society of America Bulletin* 81: 3775-3778.

Stalker, A. MacS. and Harrison, J.E., 1977: Quaternary glaciation of the Waterton-Castle River region of Alberta. *Bulletin of Canadian Petroleum Geology* 25 (4): 882-906.

Stanton, D.M., 1979: Morphology of rock glaciers in the Three Apostles area, central Sawatch Range, Colorado. *Geological Society of America, Abstracts with Programs* 11 (6): 303.

Stewart, Bruce, 1970: Park point. *Southwestern Lore* 36 (2): 21-23.

Stowe, L.G. and Teeri, J.A., 1978: The geographic distribution of C₄ species of the Dicotyledonae in relation to climate. *The American Naturalist* 112 (985): 609-623.

Streckeisen, A., 1976: To each plutonic rock its proper name. *Earth-Science Reviews* 12 (1): 1-33.

Stuckenrath, Robert, 1977: Radiocarbon: some notes from Merlin's diary. *In* Newman, W.S. and Salwen, B. (eds.), *Amerinds and their Paleoenvironments in Northeastern North America. Annals of the New York Academy of Sciences* 288: 181-188.

Stuckenrath, R., Jr. and Mielke, J.E., 1970: Smithsonian Institution radiocarbon measurements VI. *Radiocarbon* 12 (1): 193-204.

Stuckenrath, R., Miller, G.H., and Andrews, J.T., 1979: Problems of radiocarbon dating Holocene organic-bearing sediments, Cumberland Peninsula, Baffin Island, N.W.T., Canada. *Arctic and Alpine Research* 11 (1): 109-120.

Stuiver, M. and Kra, R., 1980: Proceedings of the Tenth International Radiocarbon Conference — Bern and Heidelberg. *Radiocarbon* 22 (2-3): 1-1016.

Stuiver, M. and Polach, H.A., 1977: Reporting of ^{14}C data. *Radiocarbon* 19 (3): 355-363.

Teeri, J.A. and Stowe, L.G., 1976: Climatic patterns and the distribution of C₄ grasses in North America. *Oecologia* 23: 1-12.

Ten Brink, N.W., 1973: Lichen growth rates in West Greenland. *Arctic and Alpine Research* 5 (4): 323-331.

Thorn, C.E., 1975: Influence of late-lying snow on rock-weathering rinds. *Arctic and Alpine Research* 7 (4): 373-378.

Van Vliet, Brigitte, 1980: Correlation between fragipans and permafrost - with special reference to Weichsel silty deposits in Belgium and northern France. Manuscript submitted to *Catena*, 13 pp.

Wagner, W.P. and Eschman, D.F., 1970: A probable Late Pinedale terminal moraine in Castle River Valley, Alberta: Discussion. *Geological Society of America Bulletin* 81: 3773-3774.

Wahrhaftig, C. and Cox, A., 1959: Rock glaciers in the Alaska Range. *Geological Society of America Bulletin* 70: 383-436.

Walker, P.L., 1978: Butchering and stone tool function. *American Antiquity* 43 (4): 710-715.

Wallace, R.G., 1967: Type and rates of alpine mass movement, west edge of Boulder County, Colorado Front Range. Unpublished Ph.D. Thesis, Department of Geology, Ohio State University, 200 pp.

Wardle, Peter, 1974: Alpine timberlines. *In* Ives, J.D. and Barry, R.G. (eds.), *Arctic and Alpine Environments.* Methuen & Co., Ltd., London, p. 371-402.

Washburn, A.L., 1980: *Geocryology. A Survey of Periglacial Processes and Environments.* John Wiley & Sons, New York, 406 pp.

Webber, P.J. and Andrews, J.T., 1973: Lichenometry: A commentary. *Arctic and Alpine Research* 5 (4): 295-302.

Weber, W.A., 1976: *Rocky Mountain Flora.* Colorado Associated University Press, Boulder, 479 pp.

Wedel, W.R., 1961: *Prehistoric Man on the Great Plains.* University of Oklahoma Press, Norman, 355 pp.

Whalley, W.B., 1974: Origin of rock glaciers. *Journal of Glaciology* 13 (68): 323-324.

Wheeler, R.P., 1952: A note on the "McKean Lanceolate point". *Plains Archeological Conference News Letter* 4 (4): 39-44.

_____, 1954: Two new projectile point types: Duncan and Hanna points. *Plains Anthropologist* 1: 7-14.

White, S.E., 1971: Rock glacier studies in the Colorado Front Range, 1961 to 1968. *Arctic and Alpine Research* 3 (1): 43-64.

_____, 1972: Alpine subnival boulder pavements in Colorado Front Range. *Geological Society of America Bulletin* 83: 195-200.

White, S.E., 1976a: Is frost action really only hydration shattering? A review. *Arctic and Alpine Research* 8 (1): 1-6.

_____, 1976b: Rock glaciers and block fields, review and new data. *Quaternary Research* 6 (1): 77-97.

Willard, B.E., 1979: Plant sociology of alpine tundra, Trail Ridge, Rocky Mountain National Park, Colorado. *Quarterly of the Colorado School of Mines* 74 (4): 1-119.

Williams, Jill, 1973: Neoglacial chronology of the Fourth of July Cirque, central Colorado Front Range: discussion. *Geological Society of America Bulletin* 84 (11): 3761-3766.

Worsley, Peter, 1974: Recent "annual" moraine ridges at Austre Okstindbreen, Okstindan, north Norway. *Journal of Glaciology* 13 (68): 265-277.

Wright, H.E., Jr., 1976: The dynamic nature of Holocene vegetation: a problem in paleoclimatology, biogeography, and stratigraphic nomenclature. *Quaternary Research* 6 (4): 581-596.